AERIA

ALSO OF INTEREST

AERIAL PROJECTS

by
R. A. PENFOLD

BERNARD BABANI (publishing) LTD
THE GRAMPIANS
SHEPHERDS BUSH ROAD
LONDON W6 7NF
ENGLAND

PLEASE NOTE

Although every care has been taken with the production of this book to ensure that any projects, designs, modifications and/or programs etc. contained herein, operate in a correct and safe manner and also that any components specified are normally available in Great Britain, the Publishers do not accept responsibility in any way for the failure, including fault in design, of any project, design, modification or program to work correctly or to cause damage to any other equipment that it may be connected to or used in conjunction with, or in respect of any other damage or injury that may be so caused, nor do the Publishers accept responsibility in any way for the failure to obtain specified components.

Notice is also given that if equipment that is still under warranty is modified in any way or used or connected with home-built equipment then that warranty may be void.

© 1982 BERNARD BABANI (publishing) LTD

First Published — July 1982
Reprinted — October 1988
Reprinted — November 1991

British Library Cataloguing in Publication Data
Penfold, R. A.
  Aerial projects — (BP105)
  1. Antennas (Electronics) — Amateurs' manuals
  I. Title
  621.3841'35   TK 6565.A6

ISBN 0 85934 080 5

Printed and bound in Great Britain by Cox & Wyman Ltd, Reading

PREFACE

Although the popularity of building short wave receivers and other short wave equipment has waned somewhat in recent years with the rise in availability at low cost of high quality ready-made equipment, one exception has been the all-important piece of equipment that supplies the signal to the receiver; the aerial. Aerials and aerial accessories such as tuning units and preselectors remain very popular areas of experimentation, and are something that are of interest to those with commercially produced equipment as well as to the home-constructor.

The subject of aerials is a vast one, and in this book we will mainly consider practical aerial designs that give good performance, including active aerials, loop aerials, etc., rather than going deeply into the theory of aerials. A number of aerial projects including an aerial tuning unit, a preselector, and filters are also described, and this book is primarily intended for those who like to experiment with aerials and aerial equipment, or for beginners who need guidance in the choice, construction, and installation of a suitable aerial for use on the short wave bands.

R. A. Penfold.

CONTENTS

CHAPTER 1

AERIALS

Long-Wire Aerial

A long-wire aerial is just about the most simple type of aerial that can be used for serious DXing on the short wave bands, and in most situations it is possible to accommodate an aerial of this type. This is probably why the long-wire type of aerial has been so popular for many years and shows no signs of becoming any less popular now.

In theory a long-wire aerial is a straight length of wire at least a few wavelengths long. In practice this term is used for virtually any piece of wire used as an aerial, even though it will normally be far from straight and, except perhaps on the high frequency bands, is likely to be less than a couple of wavelengths in overall length. On the low frequency short wave bands a genuine long-wire aerial is not really practical since wavelengths of around 30 to 200 metres are involved, so that an aerial wire of around 60 to 400 metres would be needed on these bands, as a minimum requirement at that!

Modern receivers have quite high sensitivities in general, and in practice a long-wire aerial about 10 to 40 metres in length is likely to give good results. In fact quite a short aerial, say about 5 metres long, and mounted indoors either around a room or in the loft is likely to provide good reception of a large number of interesting stations. However, when propagation conditions are poor and signal strengths are low the added length of a proper outdoor long-wire aerial will give substantially better results. The difference in performance is likely to be most evident at low frequencies where a short aerial will be only a small fraction of a wavelength long and will consequently be grossly inefficient. If you intend to use an aerial of this type it is therefore best to use the longest piece of aerial wire you can accommodate.

Like any aerial, a long-wire type will give best results if it is mounted as high as possible, and preferably it should be sited where it is not obstructed by buildings or other very large

1

structures or objects. Being realistic about it, it is unlikely that most radio enthusiasts will actually be able to mount the aerial on a couple of very tall aerial masts so that the wire is well clear of any obstructions. An important point to bear in mind if you do intend to employ tall aerial masts is that planning permission may be needed if the height of the masts (or mast) exceeds 10 feet above ground level. In such cases the advice of the local Council Surveyor should be sought, and if necessary planning permission should be obtained before installing the aerial supports (or support).

Many radio enthusiasts prefer not to bother with tall aerial masts, and use a relatively short aerial support or simply use any two convenient points as anchor points for the aerial wire. It is unlikely that this will give a very great reduction in performance when compared to the same length of wire mounted two or three times higher from the ground, although the reduction in performance will almost certainly be significant. Provided the aerial wire is reasonably long and a reasonable height from the ground (not much less than about 10 feet) good performance should still be obtained.

One or two points should be borne in mind when installing a long-wire aerial, and the simple installation illustrated in Figure 1 helps to demonstrate these points.

Firstly, it is essential to use suitable wire, and multistrand PVC insulated aerial wire can be obtained, or a fairly thick gauge (say about 14 to 20 swg) enamelled copper wire can be used. The insulation helps to weatherproof and protect the wire, and it also insulates it from the structure of the house at the point where it is taken into the house, which can be under a window for example. It is necessary to insulate the aerial from earth, or any earthed object such as a building, as some of the signal will otherwise leak away to earth and be wasted. This is the reason for using insulators at either end of the main section of the aerial rather than attaching the wire direct to the chimney stack and the post or tree. The two supporting lines are made from any strong man-made material (natural fibres may tend to rot) such as polypropolene twine. A pulley (which can be obtained from a chandlers or a hardware shop) is mounted at the top of the post (or on the tree) and the supporting line is

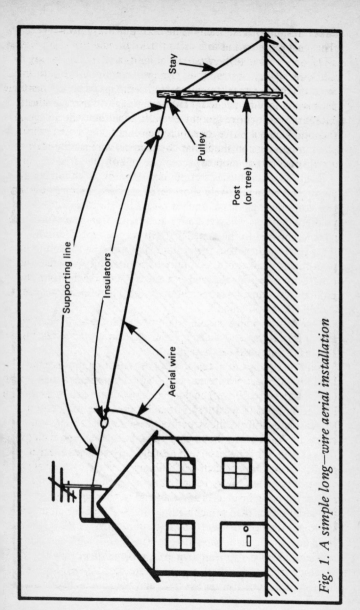

Fig. 1. A simple long—wire aerial installation

taken around this and tied-off at a convenient point lower down. This enables the aerial to be set at the desired tension, and it has to be accepted that there will be a significant amount of sag in the wire. Pulling the wire too tight will simply result in the wire snapping, either straight away or perhaps when the next high wind occurs. A certain amount of sag will not significantly affect the performance of the aerial, and neither will having one end of the aerial higher than the other.

A common problem is that of the aerial wire snapping due to the post or tree used to secure one end of the aerial moving

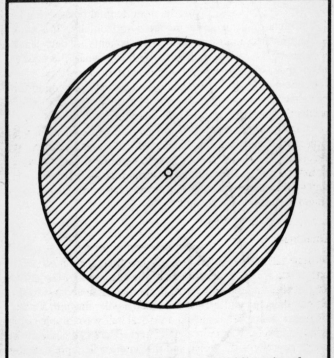

Fig. 2. The polar diagram of an omnidirectional aerial such as a half wave vertical dipole

about slightly in the wind. One way around this is to use a weight to keep the aerial under the desired amount of tension rather than securing the supporting line to the post, or a spring (of the torsion type) can be included in supporting line. Either method keeps a virtually constant tension in the aerial wire as the post or tree moves in the wind, but in practice these systems are not always fully effective and the wire can still break. This is normally caused by the supporting line becoming entangled with the pulley, or the two can become iced together in cold weather. The most reliable method in my experience is to simply leave sufficient slack in the wire!

Aerials have vertical polarisation if the aerial element or elements are mounted vertically, or horizontal polarisation if the element or elements are mounted horizontally. It is known as slant polarisation if the element or elements are between the vertical and horizontal positions. With DX signals the signals received are likely to have been transmitted with either horizontal or vertical polarisation, and propagation conditions can affect the type of polarisation of a signal. For optimum results the receiving aerial should have the same type of polarisation as the received signal, and the vertical lead-in section of the aerial can be useful when a vertically polarised signal is received. The lead-in should therefore not be thought of as a useless part of the aerial as far as signal pick-up is concerned, and a fairly long vertical lead-in section can be very advantageous under certain reception conditions.

Directivity

Most aerials receive better in some directions than in others, and a long-wire aerial is not one of the exceptions. The normal way of showing the directional properties of an aerial is to use a polar diagram, and Figure 2 shows the polar diagram for an omnidirectional aerial such as a vertical half wave dipole (which will be considered in more detail later). The small circle at the centre represents the aerial, and the outer circle represents the relative efficiency of the aerial. Since the aerial has the same efficiency in every direction a simple circle is obtained, but in most cases a somewhat more complex polar response is produced with a consequent change in the diagram. For example, a half wave dipole when mounted horizontally has peak responses at right angles to the elements, and nulls in the directions in which the elements point. This gives a polar response having two nulls and two peaks, as shown in Figure 3.

The directivity of a long wire aerial changes with variations in frequency, but there is normally a lead-in which is at least partially vertical and this tends to reduce the directivity of the aerial. Because of these two factors long-wire aerials are normally considered to be omnidirectional, and although this is not strictly accurate, the slight directivity of a practical long-wire antenna is only of accademic importance.

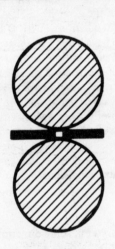

Fig. 3. The polar response of a half wave dipole showing the two peaks and the two nulls

Half Wave Dipole

A half wave dipole has the advantage over a simple long-wire aerial of greater signal output, the directional properties mentioned above, and a consequent improvement in signal to noise ratio. It has the disadvantage of being somewhat more difficult to install (although it is nevertheless quite a simple type of aerial) and it will only give near optimum results over a restricted frequency span. In practice this means that a half wave dipole has to be designed for use on one amateur or broadcast band only. The basic arrangement of a half wave dipole is illustrated in Figure 4.

As can be seen from Figure 4, this type of aerial consists of a length of wire which is broken in the middle with the two sections feeding the receiver via a 75 ohm coaxial cable. The two dipole elements must not be joined electrically. The aerial is supported

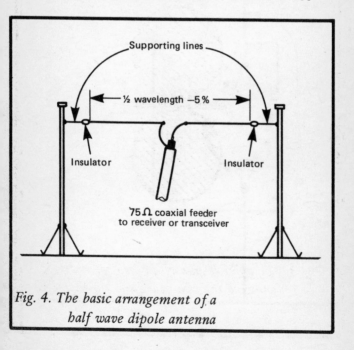

Fig. 4. The basic arrangement of a half wave dipole antenna

in the usual way using insulators, and lines made from an insulating material between the elements and the masts or other supports.

In practice you cannot simply join the two elements of the aerial to the feeder in the way shown in Figure 4 since the strain on the feeder would be so great that it would simply be ripped apart. A more satisfactory method is shown in Figure 5, but any method that prevents excessive strain on the feeder is

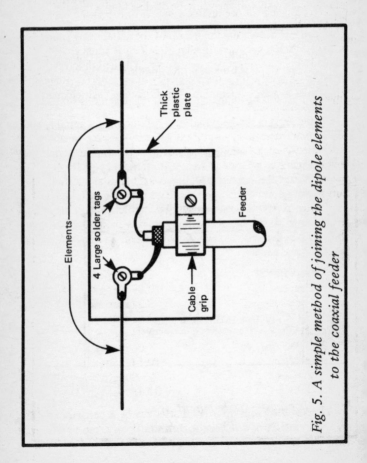

Fig. 5. A simple method of joining the dipole elements to the coaxial feeder

acceptable, provided the two dipole elements are not shorted together.

The precise length of the aerial is not exactly half a wavelength in practice as a number of factors alter the effective length of the aerial (its electrical and physical lengths are not the same). Assuming that the wire used for the aerial is a normal aerial type (such as 14 to 20swg enamelled copper wire) the total length of the aerial will need to be 5% less than half a wavelength, and each element will therefore be 5% less than a quarter wavelength.

If you are calculating the length of the aerial using frequency as the starting point, then the length in feet is equal to 468 divided by the frequency in megahertz. The length in metres is equal to 143 divided by the frequency in megahertz. Remember that this is the overall length of the aerial, and each element is only half the calculated length.

Of course, it is unlikely that you will require an aerial for use on just one frequency, and that it will be necessary for the aerial to operate over one amateur or broadcast band. The aerial is then designed to operate at the centre frequency of the band in question, and the amateur and broadcast bands are sufficiently narrow for good results to be obtained over the entire band.

The list given below shows suitable dipole element lengths for the amateur bands (including the three new bands). Note that these are the lengths for each dipole element and not the overall length of the aerial.

10 metres	2.48 metres
12 metres	2.87 metres
15 metres	3.37 metres
16.5 (17) metres	3.95 metres
20 metres	5.04 metres
29.5 (30) metres	7.06 metres
40 metres	10.14 metres
80 metres	19.59 metres
160 metres	37.63 metres

Dipoles for bands up to 40 metres can be accommodated in most back gardens without too much difficulty, but an 80 metre dipole obviously requires a fair amount of space and a 160 metre half wave dipole is around 75 metres (250 feet) in overall length.

The list shown below gives suitable dipole lengths (for each element again) for the broadcast bands, including the new 22 metre band.

11 metres	2.76 metres
13 metres	3.30 metres
16 metres	4.03 metres
19 metres	4.66 metres
22 metres	5.22 metres
25 metres	6.03 metres
31 metres	7.37 metres
41 metres	9.93 metres
49 metres	11.77 metres
60 metres	14.58 metres
75 metres	17.99 metres
90 metres	21.67 metres
120 metres	29.80 metres

Once again, most back gardens will accommodate a half wave dipole for the higher frequency bands, but for the 60, 75, 90 and 120 metre bands an aerial of this type will often be an impractical proposition.

Inverted V Aerial

This is really a modified version of the half wave dipole. This type of antenna is illustrated in Figure 6 and it should be obvious from this how the "inverted V" name is obtained.

The inverted V configuration has similar characteristics to a half wave dipole and has the obvious advantage of needing only one mast or other central support. Although at first sight it may appear to need less space than a half wave dipole this is not necessarily the case. The elements are slightly longer than for a half wave dipole, and in order to keep the elements well above ground level it is either necessary to have a tall aerial mast (especially for an aerial cut for a low frequency band) or keep the angle between the elements quite large and have very long supporting lines. This type of aerial is probably most suitable for use in situations where suitable supports for the aerial are already

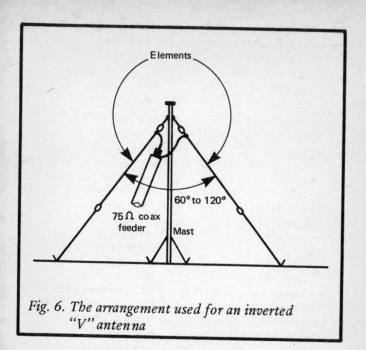

Fig. 6. The arrangement used for an inverted
"V" antenna

available or are easily improvised. For example, aerials of this
type are often installed over the pointed roof of a house (but
must be kept reasonably well clear of the roof in order to obtain
good results).

The length of an inverted V aerial in feet is equal to 486
divided by the frequency in megahertz, or in metres it is equal to
148 divided by the frequency in megahertz. This is the total
length of the two elements, and must be halved to give the
length of each element.

The lists provided below give the element lengths (not the
overall lengths) for inverted V antennas for use on the short wave
amateur and broadcast bands.

Amateur Bands

10 metres	2.56 metres
12 metres	2.97 metres

15 metres	3.49 metres
16.5 (17) metres	4.08 metres
20 metres	5.22 metres
29.5 (30) metres	7.31 metres
40 metres	10.50 metres
80 metres	20.27 metres
160 metres	38.95 metres

Broadcast Bands

11 metres	2.86 metres
13 metres	3.42 metres
16 metres	4.17 metres
19 metres	4.82 metres
22 metres	5.40 metres
25 metres	6.24 metres
31 metres	7.63 metres
41 metres	10.28 metres
49 metres	12.18 metres
60 metres	15.01 metres
75 metres	18.62 metres
90 metres	22.42 metres
120 metres	30.85 metres

Multiband Dipole

A multiband dipole uses the arrangement shown in Figure 7, and is really just three dipoles (in this example) sharing a common 75 ohm coaxial feeder. The element lengths are calculated in the same way as for a single dipole. A popular aerial of this type has the elements cut for operation on the 10, 20 and 40 metre bands, and the 40 metre band aerial also gives good results on the 15 metre amateur band (which is harmonically related to the 40 metre band, being three times higher in frequency). Thus an antenna of this type gives good results on all three high frequency amateur bands plus the 40 metre band, and does not take up a very large amount of room. For reception purposes an aerial of this type also gives good results over the broadcast bands from 11 metres to 49 metres.

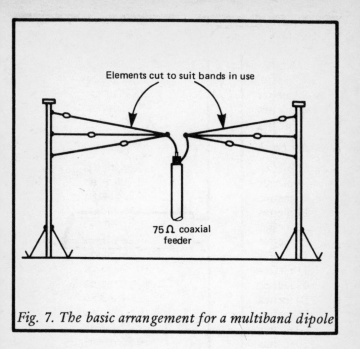

Elements cut to suit bands in use

75 Ω coaxial
feeder

Fig. 7. The basic arrangement for a multiband dipole

Folded Dipole

This is another variation on the basic dipole, and it uses the simple arrangement shown in Figure 8. The output impedance of a simple folded dipole of this type is four times higher than that of a standard half wave dipole, and the feeder is therefore 300 ohm ribbon feeder rather than the 75 ohm coaxial type used in the previous dipole designs. The length of the aerial (i.e. the distance from one end to the other and not the distance around the loop of wire) is calculated in the same way as for an ordinary half wave dipole.

In practice folded dipoles almost invariably use the method of construction shown in Figure 9, with the aerial and feeder both being constructed from 300 ohm ribbon feeder.

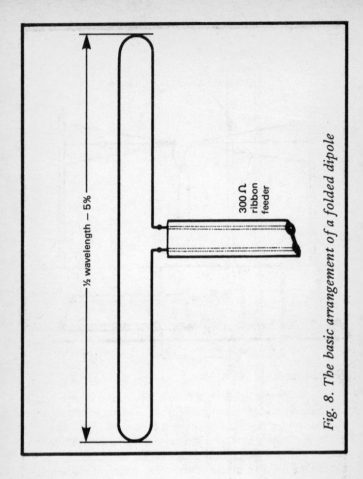

Fig. 8. The basic arrangement of a folded dipole

Windom Aerial

This is a very simple type of aerial that gives good results on the band for which it is designed, and will give useful results on other bands (especially higher frequency bands) if used with an aerial tuning unit to ensure good impedance matching between the aerial and the receiver. The main section has similar directional properties to a half wave dipole, giving

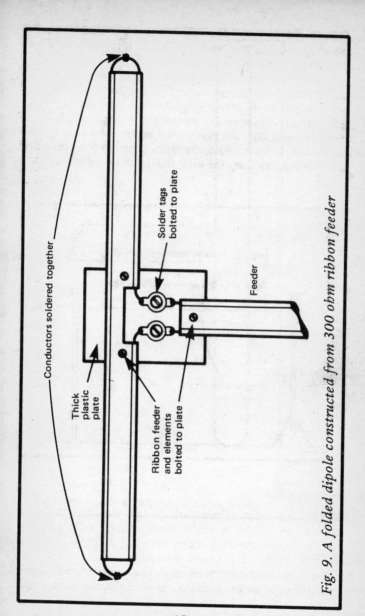

Fig. 9. A folded dipole constructed from 300 ohm ribbon feeder

reduced pick-up in the directions in which the aerial wire is pointing, and maximum pick-up and gain at right angles to the direction of the wire.

Figure 10 shows the basic arrangement of a Windom aerial, and the length of the main section of the aerial is calculated in the same way as the overall length of a half wave dipole. It differs from a dipole in that the feeder is simply a length of ordinary aerial wire, and that there is no break between the two sections of the aerial. Also, the feeder connects to a point three eights of the way along the wire, and not at the middle like a dipole.

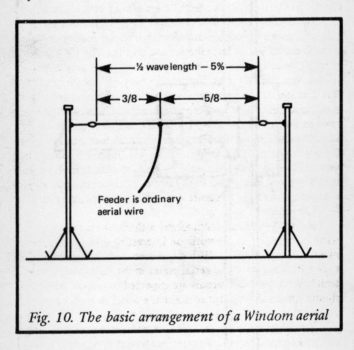

Fig. 10. The basic arrangement of a Windom aerial

Increased Gain

It is possible to obtain greater gain and directivity from a dipole antenna by the use of additional elements placed in front of and behind the dipole elements. The aerial then becomes unidirectional rather than bidirectional, and the polar response is the cardoid (heart shaped) as shown in Figure 11. The element in front of the dipole is called the director and the one behind it is called the reflector. Neither are in electrical contact with the dipole elements. Additional directors can be used to increase the gain and directivity of the aerial, but this reduces the output impedance and bandwidth of the aerial (additional directors are usually made progressively shorter to minimise the reduction in bandwidth).

Aerials of this type are a little impractical for the average short wave enthusiast due to the large size of such an aerial at the frequencies involved on the short wave bands. An aerial having a dozen or more elements may be quite manageable and easy to install if it is designed for use on the UHF TV bands, since at these frequencies the aerial elements are only a few inches long. In fact most households have an aerial of this type. But even on the 10 metre amateur band or 11 metre broadcast band an aerial of this type is quite large, and home-constructing such an aerial in a single rigid structure so that it can be easily aimed in the desired direction is not an easy task (ready-made "Beam" aerials for the HF bands can be obtained if you do not feel inclined to "do-it-yourself"). Multi-element aerials for the low frequency bands are totally impractical for most short wave enthusiasts since they require a similar amount of space to a football pitch!

Despite the difficulties involved with multi-element short wave aerials they do represent an interesting area for experimentation, and it is not difficult to erect a simple aerial of this type with the aim of the aerial preset in the direction from which the desired DX signals are expected to come. While you should obviously attempt to make the aerial as neatly and accurately as possible, it does not need to be perfect in order to give good results and prove to be a worthwhile exercise. The overall length of the dipole elements in feet is equal to 475 divided by the frequency in megahertz, or in metres it is equal to 144.5 divided by the frequency in megahertz.

The reflector is slightly larger, and can have a length equal to 500 divided by the frequency in megahertz to give an answer

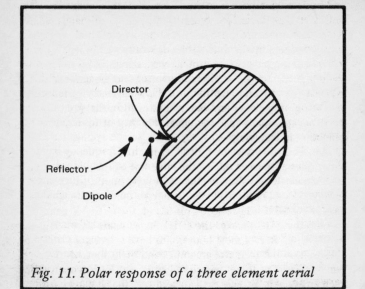

Fig. 11. Polar response of a three element aerial

in feet, or 152.25 divided by the frequency in megahertz to give an answer in metres. The director is the smallest, and can have a length equal to 455 divided by the frequency in megahertz to give an answer in feet, or 138.5 divided by the frequency in megahertz if an answer in metres is required.

The spacing between the three elements is not critical, and should be around 0.2 to 0.5 of the overall length of the dipole elements (or about 0.1 to 0.25 of a wavelength in other words). The ratio of each element's length to its diameter should be between about 250 and 500. Thus an aerial of this type, even for use on the 10 or 11 metre bands would ideally be made of thin rod or tube, but worthwhile results seem to be produced in practice using heavy gauge aerial wire. The feeder is 50 ohm coaxial cable.

Ground Plane Aerial

A ground plane antenna is an omnidirectional type that works best with low angle skywave and ground wave signals. Aerials of this type are most often employed on the VHF bands where the element sizes are quite small and the whole aerial is easily accommodated in a limited space. It works well on the VHF bands as it is normally the ground wave signal that is used (although not for DX working of course), but an aerial of this type also gives good reception of the low angle skywave used for DXing on the high frequency bands. Also, the size of a ground plane antenna for the high frequency bands is not excessive and is a practical proposition for the average back garden. A ground plane antenna for the low frequency bands would require a very high supporting mast and would not give good results as a DX aerial where good reception of high angle skywaves is required. It is best suited to the 20 metre amateur band and higher frequency bands.

Figure 12 illustrates the basic set-up for a ground plane antenna. A wooden post has a vertical aerial element clamped at the top, and this vertical element is electrically a quarter of a wavelength long. Physically it is slightly shorter than a quarter wavelength, and the length of this element is calculated in the same way as calculating the length of one element of a half wave dipole (this was covered earlier and will not be repeated here). The inner conductor of the 50 ohm coaxial feeder connects to the vertical element. The outer conductor connects to the radials, and four of these spaced at 90 degrees are sufficient. The radials are at about 45 degrees to the horizontal, and these can double as guy lines for the aerial mast. The radials are slightly longer than the vertical element, and they are the same length as for an inverted V aerial for use on the same band. Again, the method of calculating the length of the elements for this type of aerial has been covered already, and will not be covered again here.

Earth Connection

With many of the types of aerial described here an earth connection is not needed as part of the transmission line, but two exceptions are the long-wire and Windom types. With these an earth connection will usually give a considerable improvement

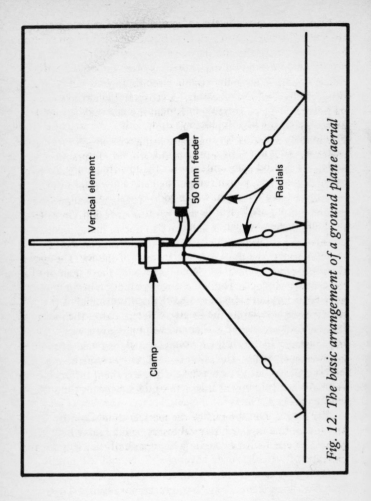

Fig. 12. The basic arrangement of a ground plane aerial

in results, especially on the lower frequency bands. It is sometimes the case that the addition of an earth connection will give improved results with other types of antenna, although this is likely to be in the form of a reduction in certain types of noise rather than an increase in signal strengths.

Of course, most communications equipment is mains powered

and for safety reasons is almost certain to have the chassis connected to the mains earth (it is not usual for communications equipment to use the alternative safety method of double insulation). However, a mains earth is often only moderately efficient, and it can under certain circumstances result in noise being coupled into the receiver. A separate, high efficiency earth may well give better results than the mains earth, and is a worthwhile area for experimentation.

An earth connection is basically just a wire which runs from the earth socket of the receiver to the ground. In practice results will not be very good if you simply strip an inch or two of insulation from the end of the lead and push it into the ground, since there will be a fairly high resistance between the ground and the wire giving a poor earth connection. In order to obtain good results it is necessary to bury a metal pipe, plate, or net (or several pipes, plates, or meshes connected together), and take the earth lead to this (or these). The larger the plate, pipe, or mesh the better, and using more than one of these also gives better results, due to a reduction in the impedance between the earth and the earth terminal of the receiver. Of course, if you have an efficient earth, then using a massive earthing plate (or whatever) will not give a vast improvement in results since there is not a great deal of room for improvement. A metal plate about 0.5 metres square, or a pipe having a similar surface area should give excellent results if buried vertically with the top at least a few inches beneath the surface level of the soil.

The lead to the terminal of the receiver should not be any longer than is absolutely necessary, and a fairly thick gauge of wire should be used. Aerial wire is perfectly suitable for the earth lead.

Do not use a water pipe as an earth as the use of plastic pipes and other factors are likely to produce poor results. There is also a slight risk of confusing a gas pipe for a water pipe, and using a gas pipe for an earth connection would be a dangerous practice and should never be done.

CHAPTER 2

ACTIVE, LOOP AND FERRITE AERIALS

Active Aerials

Any aerial that employs active (amplifying) devices could be accurately termed an active aerial, and a short length of wire feeding a wideband amplifier to compensate for the lack of signal provided by the small aerial is a simple example of an aerial of this type. However, most active aerials are slightly more complex than this, and the most common type of wideband active aerial is the dipole type.

An aerial of this type consists of two short dipole elements about one or two metres long, which is about one tenth of the size of most conventional dipole aerials for short wave use. The dipoles feed a balanced differential amplifier and the unbalanced output of the amplifier is fed to the receiver via an ordinary coaxial cable. The gain provided by the amplifier compensates for the lack of signal from the short dipole elements, and it has a high input impedance so that loading of the elements does not significantly reduce the signal level at frequencies where they provide a high output impedance.

In fact it is not true to say that the amplifier always compensates for the low signal level provided by the dipole elements since on the low frequency bands the difference in the size of an active aerial and that of a proper dipole aerial is so great that the amplifier cannot compensate for the difference in signal pick-up. This is not really of great importance though as the signal provided on the low frequency bands is still quite strong, and more than good enough to give excellent results with any reasonably sensitive communications receiver. For reception purposes the signal provided by a low frequency band dipole is often far greater than required, and, of course, an active aerial is not really suitable for transmitting.

The obvious advantage of an active aerial is that its small size enables its use in circumstances where a full size aerial would not be feasable. In fact an active aerial can be used practically anywhere, and would noramlly be used indoors rather than

22

outdoors. A less obvious advantage is that it has directional properties that are comparable to those of a conventional dipole antenna, and the small size of the aerial make it a comparitively simple matter to alter its orientation if desired. An active aerial is certainly interesting to experiment with, and in situations where space is limited it is the obvious choice.

The Circuit

The circuit diagram of the Active Aerial is shown in Figure 13, and the circuit really consists of little more than three emitter follower stages.

However, the first two common emitter stages, which are based on Tr1 and Tr2, feed the primary winding of wideband transformer T1 from their outputs, and each input is fed from one of the dipole elements. Antiphase signals are produced by the aerial elements, and these are coupled to the wideband transformer by the two emitter follower stages. The latter are needed to match the high output impedance of the dipole elements to the low input impedance of the transformer. Tr2 does not feed T1's primary winding direct from its emitter, but instead a split emitter load (R5 and R6) is used with T1 being fed from the junction of the two resistors. This gives a small amount of attenuation between Tr2's emitter and T1. Similarly, Tr1 feeds the other side of T1's primary winding via an attenuator which consists of R3, R4 and VR1: C1 is merely a DC blocking capacitor. VR1 can be used to vary the amount of attenuation provided between Tr1 and T1, and in practice it is used to precisely balance the circuit so that any signal common to both dipole elements and in phase is cancelled out by a simple phasing process. This optimises the directivity of the aerial and can help to eliminate problems with pick-up of certain types of electrical noise.

T1 provides a small voltage step-up, and C2 couples the output signal to the input of the third emitter follower stage which uses Tr3 in a conventional circuit configuration. C3 provides DC blocking at the output of the circuit and C4 is a a supply decoupling capacitor. The current consumption of the circuit is about 10mA.

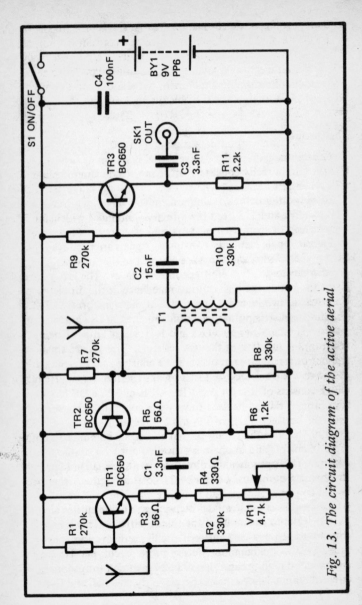

Fig. 13. The circuit diagram of the active aerial

24

Components for Active Aerial (Figure 13)
   Resistors, all 1/3 watt 5%

R1	270k	R2	330k
R3	56 ohms	R4	330 ohms
R5	56 ohms	R6	1.2k
R7	270k	R8	330k
R9	270k	R10	330k
R11	2.2k		
VR1	4.7k lin. carbon potentiometer		

   Capacitors

C1	3.3nF ceramic plate	C2	15nF ceramic plate
C3	3.3nF ceramic plate	C4	100nF polyester (C280)

   Semiconductors

Tr1	BC650	Tr2	BC650
Tr3	BC650		

   Switch

S1   SPST Miniature toggle type
   Miscellaneous
Case
0.1in matrix stripboard
Ferrite ring (see text)
24swg enamelled copper wire
Wire for dipoles
Coaxial socket (SK1)
PP6 battery and connector (PP3 style) to suit
Control knob
Wire, solder, etc.

Construction

All the small components are fitted onto a small 0.1in matrix stripboard measuring 12 strips by 21 holes using the component layout and wiring illustrated in Figure 14. This is all very straight forward and should not give any real difficulties with the exception of the wideband transformer, T1. This is home constructed, and a ½in (12.7mm) diameter ferrite ring is used as the basis of the component used in the prototype. However, any ferrite ring of around this size and intended for use in wideband applications should be perfectly suitable, and this

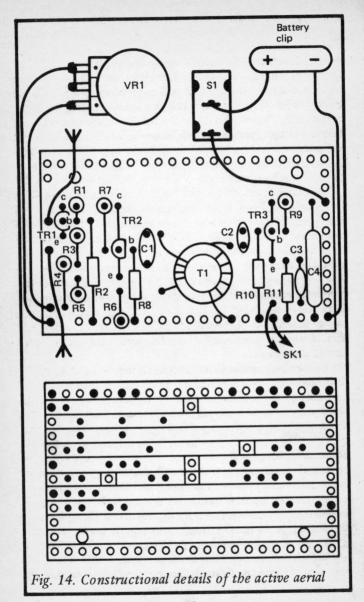

Fig. 14. Constructional details of the active aerial

26

component is not especially critical. The primary winding consists of nine turns of 24swg enamelled copper wire wound using a minimum of spacing between turns. The secondary winding consists of 22 turns of the same wire. Figure 15 illustrates the construction of this transformer. As 24swg copper wire is quite stout the windings will not tend to unwind, and the leadout wires will provide a reasonably firm mounting for the component. Despite this it is still advisable to use some epoxy adhesive (or the special "Denfix" adhesive which is available for this purpose) to secure the windings to the ferrite ring. It is also a good idea to use some epoxy adhesive to glue the transformer to the component panel.

The physical construction of the unit can take a number of forms, and the simplest one is to mount the electronics in a small case having a small hole drilled at each end. The dipole elements are then threaded through the holes (one through each hole) and connected to the component panel. The two elements should be accurately cut to the same length, and should be between one and two metres long. 20swg wire was used for the prototype aerial, but a slightly thicker gauge is equally suitable. In use the aerial is supported at the end of each dipole and at the case in the middle. A coaxial cable which should be no longer than is absolutely necessary is used to connect the output of the unit to the receiver.

An alternative method is to use metal rods or tubes as the dipole elements, and these should be no thicker than is necessary to give the whole assembly the desired rigidity. With the dipole elements firmly secured to the case (making sure they are insulated from one another and from the case if it is a metal type) it is then quite easy to install the aerial, and to change its orientation if necessary.

Another alternative is to fit dowels to the case so that the unit can be built as one rigid assembly but ordinary wire can be used for the dipole elements, the dowels providing support for these. With this method it is possible to coil the wire around the dowels so that each element can be slightly longer than the supporting dowels. Folded dipole elements can also be tried. It is usually better to experiment with methods of this type if improved performance is desired, rather than try to increase the

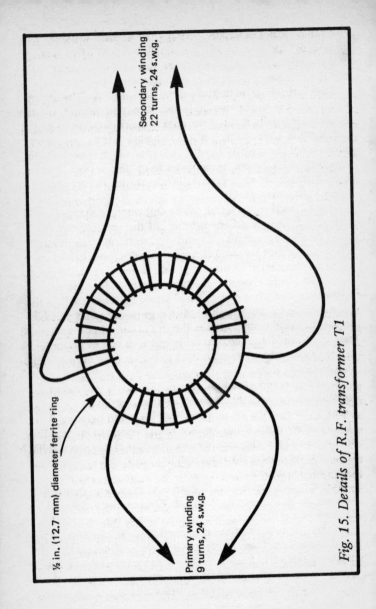

½ in. (12.7 mm) diameter ferrite ring

Secondary winding
22 turns, 24 s.w.g.

Primary winding
9 turns, 24 s.w.g.

Fig. 15. Details of R.F. transformer T1

28

gain of the amplifier section of the unit. This is simply because the amplifier inevitably produces a certain amount of noise, and increasing the amplifier section's gain gives a corresponding increase in the noise level. Thus, although weak signals may be increased in level, they are likely to be lost in the noise level and no more readily copied. Increasing the efficiency of the dipole elements will give an increase in signal strengths without changing the signal to noise ratio significantly, and is a more worthwhile area for experimentation.

Whatever constructional method is used, always keep the dipole elements the same length and as symetrical as possible.

If the aerial is to be mounted in a loft or some other place where access is difficult the battery and on/off switch can be located away from the main unit, close to the receiver. An extra lead must then be run alongside the coaxial output cable of the unit to take the positive supply to the amplifier.

In Use

In order to adjust the balance control (VR1) it is first necessary to tune the unit to a strong station that is not prone to fading. A nearby medium wave broadcast station is probably best for this. Temporarily short circuit the two dipole elements together so that the two inputs of the amplifier are fed with identical in-phase signals. With VR1 at maximum resistance a strong output signal should be obtained, and this will quickly fall off in strength as VR1 is set for a lower resistance, and then start to rise in strength. VR1 is carefully adjusted to give the lowest possible strength. If a very deep and definite null cannot be obtained this means that the unit is not functioning properly and it should be thoroughly checked for errors. With the short across the amplifier's inputs removed the unit is then ready for use.

If the unit shows signs of instability reversing the leadout wires of T1's secondary winding should rectify this.

In order to take advantage of the directional properties of the aerial it must be mounted horizontally. It can be orientated to null an interfering transmission, or a local source of interference perhaps, although it might be necessary to slant the aerial in order to obtain optimum rejection. This is necessary when trying to null a local source of interference. Good directional properties should be obtained with ground wave and low angle skywave signals, as with an ordinary dipole aerial. The aerial will be omnidirectional if it is mounted in a vertical position, and will give good reception of ground wave and low angle skywave transmissions. Results are likely to be comparitively poor with high angle skywaves though.

For best results the aerial should be kept reasonably well clear of walls, the floor, etc., although in practice this may not be feasable and it may be necessary to accept a small loss of performance because of this. An important point to bear in mind is that the aerial gives quite a strong output signal and with many receivers it will sometimes be capable of overloading the front end circuitry and causing severe cross modulation. As with a normal aerial, the RF gain control of the receiver should be used sensibly and when necessary kept below the level at which severe cross modulation begins to limit performance.

The aerial will work well over the full short wave spectrum, and will also work over the medium and long wavebands. It is not recommended for use at higher frequencies.

Simple Active Aerial

If a simple short wire, rod, or telescopic aerial is used to provide the input signal for an active aerial system it is possible to use an extremely simple circuit. In fact all that is required is a buffer stage to provide a high input impedance so that there is minimal loading on the aerial which will have a high output impedance at most frequencies. Most receivers have a low input impedance and if fed direct from a short aerial load it heavily so that the output voltage provided by the aerial is greatly reduced. Thus, although the buffer stage does not give any voltage gain (there will be a marginal voltage loss from the input to the output in fact), by reducing the loading by a substantial amount it greatly increases the signal voltage fed to the receiver. The increase in signal strength is normally greatest at the low frequency end of the short wave spectrum where a short aerial is likely to be least efficient.

A simple active aerial of this type is shown in the circuit diagram of Figure 16. This is just a simple emitter follower

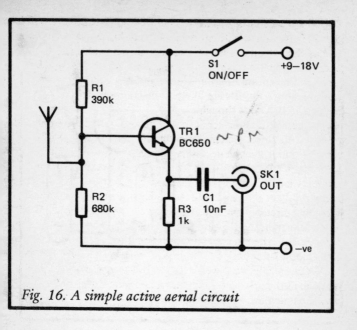

Fig. 16. A simple active aerial circuit

buffer stage fed direct from the aerial which is a rod, wire, or telescopic aerial about one or two metres in length. It is not advisable to use an aerial any longer than this as it could easily overload the unit, producing spurious signals at the output. This is especially important if the unit is used with a sensitive receiver on the high frequency bands, as it is under these conditions that overloading is most likely to be noticeable. The unit will work well from a single 9 volt battery (with a current consumption of about 4.5mA), but greater immunity to overloading can be obtained using two batteries connected in series to produce an 18 volt supply (with a current consumption of about 9mA).

The unit can be assembled on a 0.1in matrix stripboard having 11 copper strips by 13 holes using the component layout and wiring shown in Figure 17. There are no breaks in the copper strips using this layout incidentally.

Although the aerial may be very short, the unit provides quite a strong output signal and the RF gain control of the

31

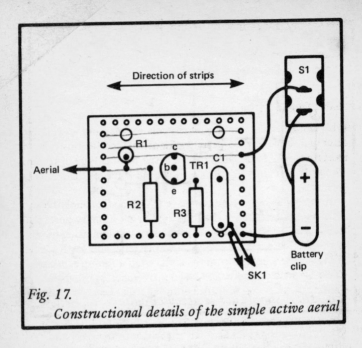

Direction of strips

Aerial

R1

R2   R3

TR1   C1

S1

+

−

Battery clip

SK1

Fig. 17.

Constructional details of the simple active aerial

receiver should not be advanced any further than is absolutely necessary as the receiver might be overloaded.

Components for Simple Active Aerial (Figure 16)

   Resistors, all 1/3 watt 5%

R1   390k   R2   680k
R3   1k
   Capacitor
C1   10nF polyester (C280)
   Semiconductor
Tr1   BC650
   Switch
S1   SPST miniature toggle type
   Miscellaneous
Case
0.1in matrix stripboard

PP6 battery and connector to suit
Aerial wire
Coaxial socket (SK1)
Connecting lead, wire, solder, etc.

Active Ferrite Aerial

It is possible to use a long wire antenna for medium wave DX reception, but there are better types of antenna for this type of reception. The two main types of aerial for this type of reception are ferrite and loop antennas, and we will consider the ferrite type first.

A ferrite aerial for medium wave DXing could simply be an ordinary ferrite aerial of the type used in an ordinary portable radio, with the low impedance secondary winding being used to couple the output of the aerial to the aerial and earth sockets of the receiver. Apart from the aerial itself a tuning capacitor would be needed, and would be connected across the main winding of the aerial transformer in the usual way. The tuning capacitor would be used to resonate the aerial at the reception frequency in order to obtain high efficiency, and this would give the advantage of added RF selectivity to the receiving system. This is one advantage of a ferrite aerial over a long wire type, the other main one being the directivity of a ferrite aerial. This sometime permits the orientation of the aerial to be adjusted to null an interfering signal while giving a strong signal from the wanted transmission. A third advantage of a ferrite aerial is simply that it is small and easy to install.

The severe drawback of the system outlined above is that even if used with a sensitive receiver it is unlikely to give good results due to the comparitively low signal level provided by a ferrite aerial. This is a problem that is easily overcome though, and it is merely necessary to use some preamplification between the aerial and the receiver. This gives a strong signal and a low noise level provided a suitable preamplifier circuit is used.

The Circuit

Figure 18 shows the circuit diagram of a simple active ferrite

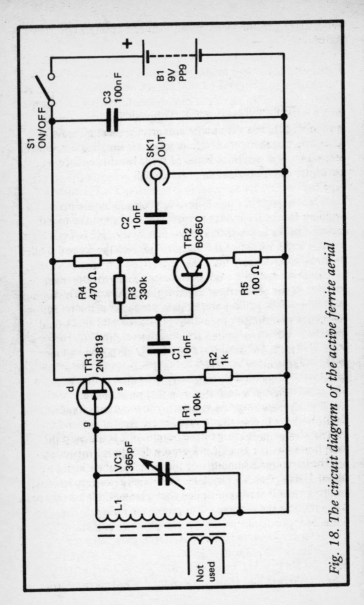

Fig. 18. The circuit diagram of the active ferrite aerial

34

aerial for use on the medium waveband and using a two stage preamplifier.

The tuned circuit is formed by the main winding on the ferrite aerial (L1) and tuning capacitor VC1. Rather than use the coupling winding on L1, the output of the tuned circuit is directly coupled to the input of a source follower buffer stage which uses JFET transistor Tr1. Although Tr1 has a voltage gain of slightly less than unity, this arrangement effectively gives a certain amount of voltage gain as it avoids the voltage step-down that would be incurred if the low impedance coupling winding of L1 was utilized.

R1 is not needed to provide gate biasing for Tr1 since a suitable DC path to earth is already provided by the main winding of L1. R1 is needed in order to "damp" the tuned circuit slightly in order to prevent instability. R2 is Tr1's load resistor and C1 couples the output of Tr1 to the second stage of amplification.

The second amplifier stage employs Tr2 in the common emitter mode. The output signal from Tr1 needs only a modest boost in order to bring it to a high enough level to adequately drive most receivers, and negative feedback is therefore applied to Tr1 by the inclusion of emitter resistor R5. This gives Tr2 a voltage gain of only about 5 times. R4 is the collector load resistor for Tr2 and R3 is the base bias resistor. R4 has been given a fairly low value as the output of the aerial is likely to feed into a fairly low impedance load, and the unit therefore needs a reasonably low output impedance in order to prevent the output signal being greatly reduced in amplitude due to loading of the output. C2 is the output coupling capacitor and C3 is a supply decoupling capacitor.

The current consumption of the circuit is quite high at about 10mA or so, and in order to obtain reasonably low running costs it is recommended that a large 9 volt battery such as a PP9 type should be used to power the unit.

Components for Active Ferrite Aerial (Figure 18)
   Resistors, all 1/3 watt 5%

R1	100k	R2	1k
R3	330k	R4	470 ohms

R5   100 ohms
    Capacitors
C1   10nF polyester (C280) C2   10nF polyester (C280)
C3   100nF polyester (C280)
VC1   365pF air spaced (Jackson type O)
    Semiconductors
Tr1   2N3819   Tr2   BC650
    Switch
S1   SPST toggle type
    Inductor
L1   MW ferrite aerial (e.g. Denco MW5FR)
    Miscellaneous
Case
Coaxial socket (SK1)
0.1in matrix stripboard
Control knob
PP9 battery and connectors to suit
Mounting clip for aerial (see text)
Wire, solder, etc.

Construction

Most of the components are accommodated on a 0.1in matrix
stripboard having 14 holes by 12 strips using the component
layout and wiring illustrated in Figure 19. If the ferrite aerial is
to be fitted inside the case it is essential to use a non-metalic
type as a metal case would shield the aerial and prevent any
signal pick-up. The aerial is mounted at any convenient place on
the case using either a 10mm (or thereabouts) 'P' type cable grip,
or proper ferrite rod mounting clips if these can be obtained. L1
is wound using Litz wire, but there should be no problems when
connecting it into circuit as the leadout wires are ready tinned
with solder. The output of the unit is coupled to the receiver via
a twin cable which would ideally be a coaxial type so that there
is no significant signal pick-up in this lead, and a well defined null
can be obtained by rotating the unit if necessary. However, in
practice any signal pick-up in the connecting cable is not likely
to be sufficient to seriously affect the performance of the aerial,
and an ordinary twin cable should give good results. Whatever

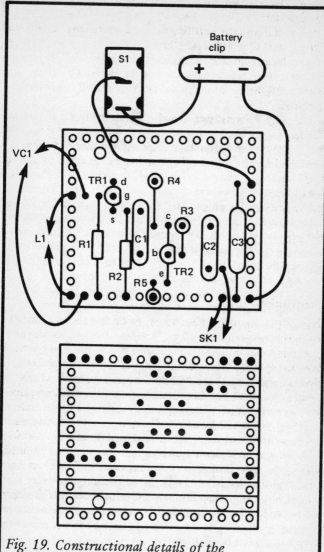

*Fig. 19. Constructional details of the
active ferrite aerial*

37

type of cable is used, use a maximum length of no more than about 1 metre.

A slight drawback to fitting the ferrite aerial inside the case is that this makes it necessary to move the whole unit in order to give the aerial the required orientation. This can be overcome by fitting the ferrite aerial on top of the case in a rotating mount, and this is not as difficult to achieve as it might at first appear.

Probably the most simple way of achieving this is to mount a standard jack socket on top of the case, and connect this to the two points on the circuit board that would otherwise connect direct to L1. The ferrite aerial can then be mounted on and connected to a standard jack plug which plugs into the socket on top of the case, giving the required rotating mount. The aerial can be glued to the plug (which should be a type having a plastic outer cover) using a gap filling adhesive such as an epoxy type, and a file is used to make a groove for the aerial in the rear end of the cover. The leads from L1 fit through two small holes drilled in the plastic cover, and these are then connected to the two tags of the main part of the plug. Trim the ends of the leadout wires so that only the last few millimetres are not insulated, and there is no risk of a short circuit occuring when the outer casing of the plug is screwed on and the two leadout wires become twisted together.

If this method of mounting is used it is possible to use a metal case, and this will screen the circuitry from unwanted signal pick-up. However, make sure that the jack socket is connected to the component panel in such a way that the case connects to the negative supply rail, and not to the gate of Tr1.

In use VC1 is simply adjusted to peak received signals, and the aerial or the unit as a whole (as appropriate) can be rotated to peak the wanted signal or null an interfering signal, as required. VC1 gives coverage of slightly more than the full medium wave-band, and the position of L1 on the ferrite rod is not very critical, although it may not be possible to obtain full medium wave coverage if it is either right in the middle of the rod or only partially on the rod. It is advisable to tape L1 to the rod so that it cannot slip out of position.

Incidentally, the null is produced with the ferrite rod pointing

n the direction of the station, and the signal peaks with the rod
at right angles to this.

1.6 to 4.5 MHz Operation

Ferrite aerials will operate reasonably efficiently at higher
frequencies than those found on the medium waveband, although
at frequencies of more than a few megahertz the efficiency of a
ferrite aerial, even using an appropriate grade of ferrite rod, gives
a level of performance that is less than that obtained using a
simple telescopic aerial. Good results can be obtained at
frequencies of up to about 4 to 5 MHz using readily available
components, and aerials of this type give quite good results on
the 160 and 80 metre amateur bands.

The medium wave active ferrite aerial design can be made to
operate over a frequency range of about 1.6 to 4.5MHz simply
by removing about 12mm of the main winding of L1 (i.e. remove
sufficient turns to reduce the length of the winding from about
19mm to approximately 7mm). The amount of the coil that
needs to be removed is not very critical since the coverage can
be adjusted somewhat by altering the position of the coil on the
ferrite rod, and the coverage is more than adequate to cover the
160 and 80 metre bands anyway.

It is likely that an increase in the preamplifier gain will give
improved results, and this can easily be achieved by making R5
somewhat lower in value, say about 39 ohms. Using an even
lower value will give an even greater boost in gain, but it is probable
that a value much lower than 39 ohms will cause instability
and make the aerial unusable. It is also possible that boosting
the gain further would give a high noise level, and would not
actually give improved results even if no problems with
instability should arise.

Loop Aerial

A loop aerial, as implied by its name, consists of a loop of wire,
although a practical loop aerial for the medium waveband does
not consist of just a single loop, and is really a large, air cored
coil. The larger the loop or coil, the larger the signal obtained,

but in practice this type of aerial is only normally used indoors, and a diameter of about one metre is the maximum that can be used and accommodated conveniently. An aerial of this size gives less signal strength than an average sized longwire antenna, but it still gives results that are more than adequate provided an insensitive receiver is not being used. The advantage of a loop aerial for medium wave DXing is that it gives a higher signal to noise ratio than a longwire type, and like a ferrite aerial it has directional properties that enable interfering signals to be nulled. A practical loop antenna seems to have better defined directional properties than those of a normal ferrite aerial, although this advantage is at the expense of the greater size and inconvenience of a conventional loop antenna. In common with a ferrite aerial, loop antennas are normally tuned by means of a tuning capacitor connected in parallel with the loop so that the aerial is brought to resonance at the reception frequency, giving good efficiency and increased RF selectivity.

Conventional Loop

A conventional loop aerial consists of typically 6 turns of about 20swg enamelled copper wire on a 1 metre diameter or 1 metre square former, with the coil being scramble wound. In practice it is much easier to build a square former than it is to construct a round one, and a square former can be made from two pieces of (about) 25 x 50mm timber joined to form an "X" shape. The coil is then wound around the ends of the pieces of timber, keeping the wire as tight as possible. The tuning capacitor, which can be a twin gang 365pF air spaced type with the two sections used in parallel, is mounted towards the middle of the assembly. The main winding of the aerial connects across the tuning capacitor, keeping the leads from the coil to the tuning capacitor as short as possible. Epoxy adhesive is used to bond the coil to the pieces of timber so that the coil does not tend to unwind itself.

It is not a good idea to take the output signal from direct across the coil and tuning capacitor because the signal here is at a very high impedance and would be a very poor match for the low input impedance of most receivers. Instead, a low impedance coupling coil should be used, and a single turn coil should give good results. As with the main coil, some epoxy adhesive is used to bond this in place. The coupling coil is taken to a length of coaxial cable which is used to take the output of the aerial to the receiver, and the coaxial cable should be secured to the frame of the aerial so that movement of the aerial does not cause the joints to fatigue and eventually break. The cable can be held in place using either a staple or insulation tape.

The aerial must be mounted vertically, and as it is a directional type it should really be fitted with a rotatable mount of some kind. It does not matter whether the aerial is mounted with the cross pieces forming an "X" shape, or a "+" shape, it is merely necessary for the aerial to be mounted vertically. In practice it is probably easier to mount the unit with the cross pieces forming an "+" shape, as the rod supporting the unit can then be fixed to the vertical cross piece. The bottom part of the rod can fit into a hole drilled in a large block of wood, or something of this nature, but it must have a fairly large base area and be round or square so that it provides a stable base for the aerial.

If the main coil is wound neatly, with the turns placed side by side, it will be necessary to use an extra turn on this winding (making a total of seven turns) since this will reduce the self capacitance of the coil. A 500pF tuning capacitor should then be adequate to tune the aerial over the full medium waveband.

In use the aerial should be found to give quite a well defined null, and should enable quite strong interfering signals to be virtually eliminated. Of course, occasionally the wanted transmission and the interfering one will be nulled at virtually the same setting, and then the directional properties of the aerial will be of little or no help. However, this does not often happen, and the directional properties will normally be helpful. Maximum pick-up is obtained when the coil is pointed towards the source of the transmission, and minimum pick-up is at right angles to this. Figure 20 shows the directional properties of both ferrite and loop aerials. Of course, both aerials have two peak responses at 180 degrees to one another, and two nulls at 180 degrees to one another.

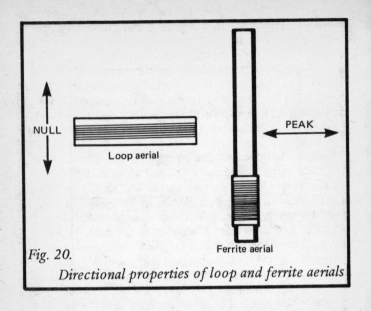

NULL

PEAK

Loop aerial

Ferrite aerial

Fig. 20.

Directional properties of loop and ferrite aerials

Active Loop Aerial

It is possible to use a fairly small coil in a loop aerial, say around 150 to 300mm in diameter, but this gives a comparitively low output signal level and may prove inadequate with many receivers. This can be overcome by using a stage of amplification between the aerial and the receiver, as in the case of an active ferrite aerial. Less gain is necessary though as a small loop aerial has a higher output than a ferrite aerial. In fact a buffer amplifier to match the high output impedance of the aerial to the low input impedance of the receiver is all that is required.

Figure 21 shows the circuit diagram of a simple active loop aerial. The buffer stage simply consists of a JFET source follower stage with its input fed direct from the loop aerial. L1 biases the input of Tr1 and VC1 is the tuning capacitor. VC1 does not give quite enough maximum capacitance to tune the aerial to the low frequency limit of the medium waveband, and C1 must be switched into circuit using S1 in order to enable the low frequency end of the band to be received properly. R1 is the

42

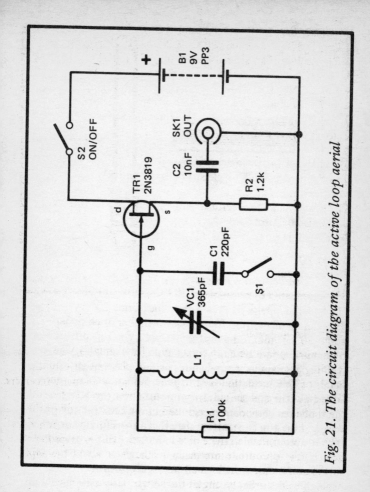

Fig. 21. The circuit diagram of the active loop aerial

source load for Tr1 and C2 provides DC blocking at the output. A small (PP3 size) 9 volt battery is an adequate power source for the circuit as the current consumption is only around 2mA.

Components for Active Loop Aerial (Figure 21)
  Resistors, both 1/3 watt 5%

R1	100k		R2	1.2k

Capacitors
C1   220pF ceramic plate   C2   10nF polyester (C280)
VC1   365pF air spaced (Jackson type 0)
   Semiconductor
Tr1   2N3819
   Miscellaneous
20swg enamelled copper wire (4 oz. is sufficient)
Coaxial socket (SK1)
Case
Materials for aerial frame and base
Two miniature SPST toggle switches (S1 and S2)
Control knob
PP3 battery and connector to suit
0.1in matrix stripboard
Wire, solder, etc.

Construction

The aerial coil (L1) consists of 20 turns of about 20swg
enamelled copper wire on a former measuring 200 by 150mm.
This can be made from four pieces of timber or chipboard
about 50 x 19mm using butt joints and a good quality adhesive
of an appropriate type (an epoxy type for example). The
winding is scramble wound and is held in place either using
bands of PVC insulation tape or generous amounts of epoxy
adhesive. The coil should by no means cover the 50mm width of
the timber or chipboard pieces used in the construction of the
coil, and the top and bottom panels can therefore be drilled to
take the rod on which the coil is mounted. This is fitted into a
hole of the appropriate size made in a large wooden base block.
   Figure 22 shows the layout and wiring of the component
panel, plus the other wiring of the aerial. The board has 11
copper strips by 13 holes and there are no breaks in the strips.
Construction of the board and wiring of the unit are quite straight
forward. The electronics could be accommodated inside the coil
framework, but this method was not used on the prototype and
the component panel, controls, output socket and battery were
fitted into a separate case. This is connected to the coil via an
ordinary (figure of 8) twin lead, and not a coaxial type (which
would have excessive capacitance). Pick-up in this connecting

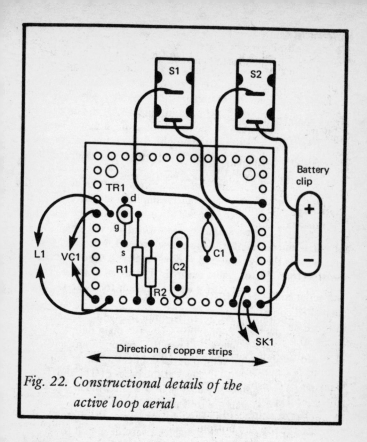

*Fig. 22. Constructional details of the
active loop aerial*

lead impairs the directional properties of the aerial somewhat, and
this is the main reason for keeping this lead as short as possible.

The unit is used just like an ordinary loop antenna, with VC1
being used to peak received signals and C1 being switched in
using S1 when necessary. With both this aerial and the one
featured earlier, the tuning is quite "sharp" and the tuning control
requires careful adjustment. With this aerial or the loop one
described earlier it may even be found beneficial to fit a slow
motion drive to the tuning capacitor.

45

Differential Loop Aerial

This is an unusual loop aerial design for use on the medium waveband in that it is designed to have a fairly wide bandwidth so that no tuning control is needed, it uses a small loop, and has excellent directional characteristics that enable a very deep null to be obtained if desired. The circuit diagram of the unit is shown in Figure 23, and as can be seen from this, the circuit is based on a "long tailed pair" differential amplifier. Tr1 and Tr2 are used in the differential amplifier, and Tr3 is employed as an emitter follower buffer stage at the output.

L1 is the aerial coil, and this feeds direct into the inputs of the differential amplifier. A differential amplifier amplifies the voltage difference placed across its two inputs, and signals produced by L1 give a suitable potential difference which gives anti-phase output signals at the collectors of Tr1 and Tr2. In this case it is the signal at Tr2's collector that is used, and the one at Tr1's collector is just ignored. The signal at the collector of Tr2 is fed to the output by way of emitter follower Tr3 and DC blocking capacitor C2.

The point of using a differential amplifier is that signals picked-up in the leads connecting L1 to the main unit will be identical (or near enough for all practical purposes anyway). In other words, signals picked-up in the connecting cable will produce identical voltage changes at the bases of Tr1 and Tr2, and will fail to produce any change in the potential at Tr2's collector. These signals are thus phased out by the use of this balanced input system, and they do not impair the directional properties of the aerial. This enables a very deep null to be obtained if desired. Note that Tr1 and Tr2 do not need to be a matched pair since a great deal of negative feedback is used in the circuit and this renders any differences in current gain unimportant.

The aerial is tuned to resonance at roughly the centre of the medium waveband by the input capacitance of the amplifier. The input impedance of Tr1 and Tr2 is far less than that obtained using a JFET input stage, and the loading on L1 is also heavier than if a low impedance coupling winding was to be used. The damping effect this has on L1 broadens its response

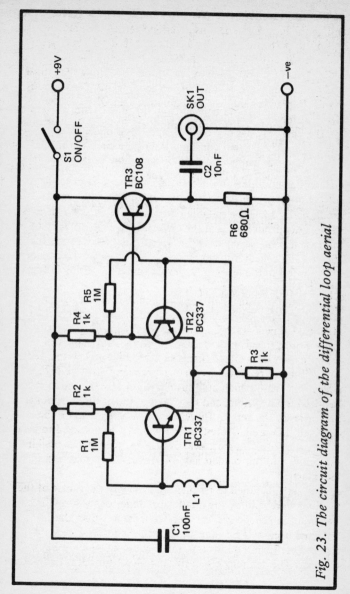

Fig. 23. The circuit diagram of the differential loop aerial

so that it does not have a very pronounced peak in its response, unlike the loop aerial designs described earlier. There is some fall off in performance at the band edges, but the aerial seems to give perfectly adequate results over the entire medium waveband. The signal provided by the unit is less strong than most active medium wave aerials, but the aerial seems to give good results in practice and when used with a Trio QR666 receiver never seemed to give inadequate gain.

The unit only has one control, and this is merely on/off switch S1. The current consumption of the circuit is around 10mA, and this can be provided by a medium or large size 9 volt battery such as a PP6 or PP9 type.

Components for Differential Loop Aerial (Figure 23)
    Resistors, all 1/3 watt 5%

R1	1M	R2	1k
R3	1k	R4	1k
R5	1M	R6	680 ohms

   Capacitors

C1	100nF polyester (C280)
C2	10nF polyester (C280)

   Semiconductors

Tr1	BC337	Tr2	BC337
Tr3	BC108		

   Switch

S1   SPST miniature toggle type
   Miscellaneous
Case
0.1in matrix stripboard
Materials for aerial frame
4 oz. 20swg enamelled copper wire (for L1)
Coaxial socket (SK1)
PP6 battery and connector to suit
Wire, solder, etc.

Construction

The aerial coil is exactly the same as the one employed in the previous loop aerial design (the "Active Loop Aerial"), and mechanically the two units are very much the same. The 0.1 in matrix stripboard layout for the "Differential Loop Aerial" is shown in Figure 24, and requires a board having 19 holes by 11 copper strips. Construction of the board should not give any difficulties, but make sure that you do not omit the single break in the copper strips.

In order to obtain a deep null from the unit is is important to use a coaxial output cable, or (as is the case with any loop aerial) it might be better to use a balanced feeder, especially if the receiver has an input for this type of feeder (which, unfortunately, many do not). Pick-up in the output lead is not normally a real problem with loop aerials as the lead is carrying a low impedance signal, and the output of an active loop aerial can be very low indeed. However, in order to obtain a really deep null so that strong heterodynes can be eliminated it is probably worth experimenting a little to see what gives best results with the particular equipment in use.

Tilting

It may well be found that with any loop aerial a deep null can be obtained on some stations while on others the peak and null are hardly noticeable. The shallowness of the null is due to a twisted or rotated wavefront, and a deep null can usually be obtained in such cases by tilting the aerial towards or away from the source of the transmission. In practice it is necessary to very carefully adjust both the rotation and the tilt of the aerial in order to obtain a really deep null as both are quite critical.

It would obviously be impractical to hold a loop aerial with the correct degree of tilt for very long, and as quite a large amount of tilt will often be needed a simple solution such as the use of a wedge will often prove inadequate. It is therefore necessary to either build a special mounting for the aerial, or simply make do with whatever null the basic aerial produces (which is often adequate in practice). A fork type mounting is probably the best solution if a special mount is made, since this leaves the weight of the aerial over the base section and does not make it physically unstable. Figure 25 illustrates the basic

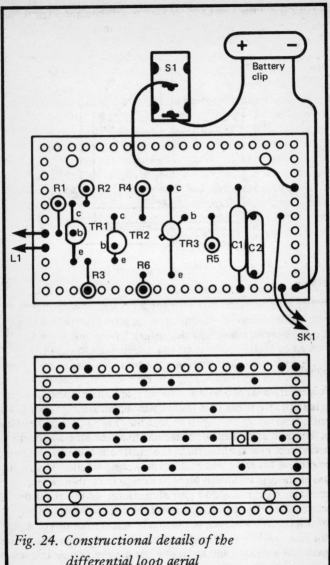

Fig. 24. Constructional details of the differential loop aerial

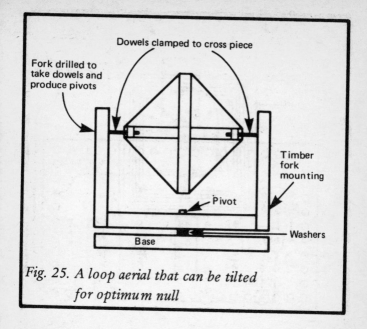

Fig. 25. A loop aerial that can be tilted for optimum null

arrangement of a fork type mounting.

Spiral Loop

A spiral loop enables an even deeper null to be obtained, and it is basically the same as an ordinary loop, but the turns of the coil are wound inside each other so that they are all on a single plane. A loop of this type can be based on a piece of plywood or the usual timber cross pieces, with the small nails or tacks being used to provide "posts" for the coil to be wound around. Figure 26 shows the general arrangement of a spiral loop. If a coupling coil is required it is added towards the inner part of the main winding, between turns, on four additional nails or tacks. A spiral loop needs to be made very well and accurately (so that the turns really are on a single plane) if the full advantage of the deep null is to be obtained (which is not quite as easy as it may at first appear), and even then the advantage of a spiral over a

51

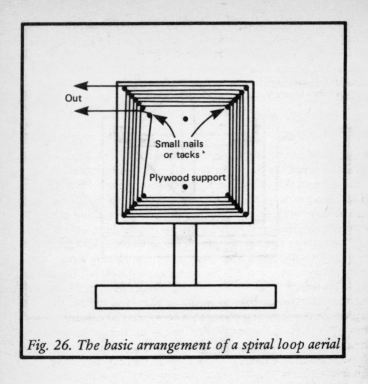

Fig. 26. The basic arrangement of a spiral loop aerial

conventional loop only seems to be marginal.

SW Operation

Loop aerials will operate on the short wave bands, although they need fewer turns in order to produce resonance at the higher frequencies involved, and this gives reduced signal pick-up. The directional properties of a loop aerial seem to be reduced at high frequencies unless a tilting aerial is used, and in order to obtain a null it will need to spend most of its time in a practically horizontal position. A loop aerial requires comparatively little space for reception at short wave frequencies up to about 4.5MHz, but I would not recommend this type of aerial for serious DX work or use at higher frequencies.

The active loop antenna described earlier can be made to operate over a range of about 1.6 to 4.5MHz by reducing the number of turns on the coil from twenty to seven. The differential loop aerial design will work well on the 160 metre band if the number of turns on the aerial coil is reduced to about twelve, or on the 80 metre band using about seven turns.

Long Wave Operation

A loop aerial can be made to operate on the long wave band quite easily, and the coil needs about three to four times as many turns as for medium wave operation. It would be more practical to use 24swg wire for a long wave aerial rather than the 20swg wire used in the medium wave designs. The signal pick-up of a long wave loop of this type is higher than that of a medium wave loop due to the larger number of turns on the aerial coil. A medium wave loop can be tuned down to frequencies within the long wave spectrum by means of additional tuning capacitance, but the value needed is around 2.7nF to 10nF for the designs described here, and this makes it necessary to choose an additional tuning capacitor value that brings resonance on the desired channel, with the ordinary tuning capacitor being used as the fine tuner to peak the aerial on that channel. Variable capacitors giving a large enough capacitance swing to permit continuous coverage using this method are not available and the additional capacitor must be a fixed type.

Finally, it is not possible to use a loop aerial properly with a receiver having a built-in ferrite aerial. The ferrite aerial will tend to reduce or eliminate the null of the loop aerial, and it is likely that the additional output of the loop will simply overload the receiver anyway.

CHAPTER 3

AERIAL ACCESSORIES

HF Bands Preselector

The performance of many short wave receivers, especially the simpler and older types, tends to be noticeably inferior on the high frequency bands when compared to the low frequency bands performance. This is unfortunate since high sensitivity is probably more valuable on the high frequency bands than it is on the low frequency ones, since QRM often makes high sensitivity unusable on the low frequency bands, but is generally less troublesome on the high frequency ones. It is not just the sensitivity that tends to reduce on the higher frequency bands though, and image rejection normally degrades severely also.

Image rejection is very important, since without any a superhet receiver will receive on two channels simultaneously. One channel is the main response of the receiver, and the other is the image response. The image is usually higher than the main response (although it can be at a lower frequency) and is separated from the main response by double the intermediate frequency of the receiver. For a receiver with a standard intermediate frequency of around 470kHz this results in the image response being less than 1MHz away from the main response. This makes it quite easy to obtain good rejection of the image response at low frequencies of just a few megahertz where the frequency difference between the main and image responses is quite large in comparison to the reception frequency. At higher frequencies of around 15 to 30MHz the difference in the frequencies of the two responses becomes small when compared to the reception frequency, and the fairly wide bandwidth of the aerial tuned circuits gives relatively little image rejection. In fact the level of image rejection on the high frequency bands if an intermediate frequency of about 470kHz is used is likely to be no more than about 20dB (in other words the main response will be no more than about ten times more sensitive than the image response). At the upper limit of the short wave spectrum (30MHz) the level of image rejection could quite easily be almost zero with a simple superhet design!

A preselector can often give a very worthwhile improvement in both sensitivity and image rejection when it is used for high frequency bands reception with a simple or older short wave set. A preselector is simply an RF amplifier which includes frequency selective circuitry so that it reduces spurious responses as well as providing increased sensitivity. It must be stressed that adding a preselector to a simple receiver will not give a vast improvement in either sensitivity or image rejection, but it will normally improve both by about 20dB, although the improvement in image rejection is likely to be somewhat less than this on the highest frequency bands. Not a vast improvement, but often enough to give a very noticeable improvement in results.

It must also be pointed out that many modern short wave receivers have high intermediate frequencies or first intermediate frequencies in the case of multiconversion types, and this gives excellent image rejection. Modern sets also usually employ devices in the RF and mixer circuitry that give high sensitivity and a low noise level. A preselector is unlikely to be of any benefit at all with a receiver of this type.

This preselector is tunable over an approximate frequency range of 10 to 30 MHz, and it therefore covers all the HF broadcast and amateur bands. By using a Range 3T coil in place of the specified Range 5T type it will cover a frequency span of about 1.6 to 5 MHz, and using a Range 4T coil gives a frequency coverage of approximately 5 to 14MHz. Thus, by using plug-in coil bandchanging or including bandswitching the unit could be made to cover the entire short wave spectrum. However, most sets have good sensitivity and image rejection on the low frequency bands, and it is doubtful if this modification would be worthwhile in most cases. The unit is powered from an internal 9 volt (PP6 size) battery which provides many hours of operation before replacement becomes necessary since the current consumption of the unit is only about 5 milliamps.

The Circuit

Figure 27 shows the full circuit diagram of the HF Bands
Preselector. This is basically just a hybrid cascade amplifier
using a common source JFET amplifier (Tr1) driving a common
base amplifier (Tr2)

T1 is the tuned input transformer, and the main winding
of this plus VC1 form the tuned circuit which gives the
additional RF selectivity provided by the unit. The aerial
signal is coupled into the tuned circuit via a low impedance
primary winding on T1. T1 also has a low impedance secondary
winding which would normally be used to couple the output of
the transformer to the input of a bipolar transistor amplifier.
This winding is not used in this circuit because the amplifier
has a JFET input stage, and this has a very high input impedance
which will directly match the high output impedance of the
tuned circuit. The tuned circuit is therefore directly coupled
to the gate of Tr1, and the tuned winding of T1 provides the
gate bias for Tr1. R3 is the source bias resistor and C2 is its
bypass capacitor.

Tr2 has its base terminal biased by R1 and R2, and C1
provides an AC path to earth for Tr2's base. The output at the
drain terminal of Tr1 is direct coupled to the input of Tr2,
which is its emitter terminal. L1 is the load for Tr2, and C3 is th
output coupling capacitor. C4 is the only supply decoupling
component that is needed and S1 is the on/off switch.

Components for HF Bands Preselector (Figure 27)
  Resistors, all 1/3 watt 5%

R1	3.9k	R2	4.7k
R3	390 ohms		

  Capacitors

C1	100nF polyester (C280)
C2	10nF ceramic plate
C3	10nF ceramic plate
C4	100nF polyester (C280)
VC1	365pF air spaced (Jackson type 0)

  Semiconductors

Tr1	2N3819	Tr2	BC108

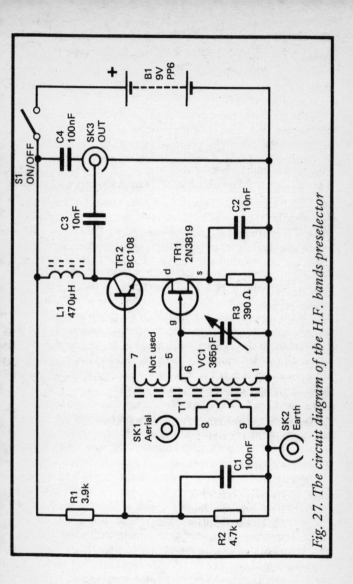

Fig. 27. The circuit diagram of the H.F. bands preselector

57

Inductors

T1   Denco blue aerial coil for transistor useage, Range 5T
L1   470μH (0.47mH) RF choke

Switch

S1   SPST miniature toggle type

Miscellaneous

Case
0.1in matrix stripboard
B9A valveholder (coilholder)
PP6 battery and connector to suit
Two wander sockets (SK1 and SK2) and one coax socket (SK3)
Control knob
Wire, solder, etc.

Construction

The unit can have most of the components fitted on a 0.1in
matrix stripboard having 14 copper strips by 14 holes using the
component layout and method of wiring shown in Figure 28.
The board is very easy to construct as there are no breaks in the
copper strips, no link wires, and few components to fit into place
The two mounting holes are 3.3mm in diameter and will accept
either 6BA or M3 mounting bolts. Stripboard is not available
in the specified size and it is therefore necessary to cut a board
down to the correct size using a hacksaw.

For best results the circuit should be housed in a metal case
so that all the wiring is screened. This prevents an effective
reduction in the selectivity of the unit due to signal pick-up in
the wiring following the tuned circuit. The two controls are
mounted on the front panel, and a slight complication here is
the unusual mounting arrangement of the tuning capacitor (VC1
This requires three 4BA screws which pass through holes in the
front panel of the case and into threaded holes in the front plate
of the component. If this method of mounting is used it is
possible to make a paper template to help with the correct
positioning of the three mounting holes in the front panel. The
template is made simply by taking a small sheet of paper, makin
a hole about 7mm in diameter at the centre, and then fitting
this over the spindle of the capacitor and onto the front plate of

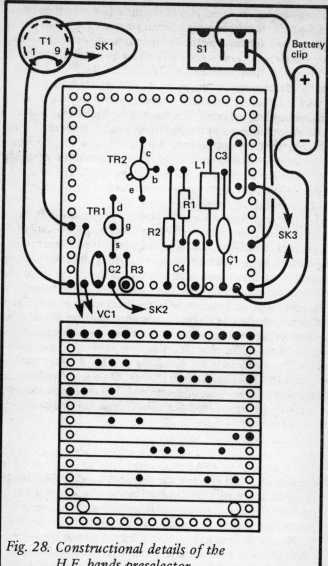

*Fig. 28. Constructional details of the
H.F. bands preselector*

the component. The positions of the three holes can then be punched into the paper using a pencil point.

A simple alternative method of mounting the capacitor is to drill a single, central mounting hole about 14mm in diameter, and then glue the component in place behind this using a high quality adhesive such as an epoxy or cynoacrylate type.

SK1 and SK2 are fitted on the rear panel of the case, and T1 can also be mounted here. This component has a mounting thread moulded into one end of the coil former, and it is supplied with a suitable plastic mounting nut. A mounting hole about 6.5mm in diameter is required for T1. Do not overtighten the mounting nut, which can be tightened sufficiently by hand. Tightening it any more than this could easily result in one or both of the plastic screwthreads being damaged.

In order to complete the unit it then only remains to fit the point-to-point style wiring, and this is very straight forward as there is only a small amount of wiring of this type. Apart from the leads to S1 and the battery clip this wiring all carries high frequency RF signals and should be kept as short as possible. A PP6 battery, incidentally, uses the common PP3 type battery connector. Connections can be made direct to the pins of T1, but great care must be taken if this is done since the plastic coil former will tend to melt almost as soon as the soldering iron is applied to one of the pins. It is therefore essential to make the soldered connections to the pins fairly swiftly. A better method is to fit a B9A valveholder onto the base of the coil (which is designed to plug into one of these), and then the connections can be made to the tags of the coilholder without any danger of damaging the coil.

In Use

The aerial connects to SK1 of the preselector and SK3 connects to the aerial and earth sockets of the receiver by way of a length of coaxial cable. Do not use a cable any longer than is really necessary, and the cable should be no more than about 1 metre long. The output lead must connect the chassis (earth) of the preselector to the earth terminal of the receiver, as well as the non-earthy output of the preselector to the aerial socket of the receiver if good results are to be obtained. Coaxial cable is used so that there is no signal pick-up in the connecting cable which would effectively reduce the extra RF selectivity provided by the unit.

VC1 is the tuning control and must be adjusted to peak received signals. The bandwidth of the unit is invariably fairly wide, and small changes in the setting of the receiver's tuning control are unlikely to merit any adjustment to VC1. However, if VC1 is peaked at one end of an amateur or broadcast band, it is likely that some slight readjustment will be needed if the receiver is later used at the other end of the band.

The unit should be found to give a reasonable boost in signal strengths, and the "S" meter should indicate a boost of a few "S" points.

The adjustable core of T1 is fully screwed in by the coil manufacturer (for packing purposes), and it must be set at a position that gives the appropriate frequency coverage. In this particular case it is unlikely that the coil will need any adjustment in order to obtain satisfactory coverage, but the core can, of course, be adjusted if the unit has a significant lack of coverage at one end of the tuning range.

Variable Aerial Attenuator

Having probably spent a great deal of time and effort to obtain the strongest possible aerial signal it may seem rather stupid to use an attenuator of some kind to reduce the strength of the signal fed to the receiver. However, there are occasions when very strong aerial signals can overload the input stages of a receiver with a consequential severe reduction in the performance of the set. This problem is more common on the broadcast bands, where there are often a large number of very powerful transmissions, than it is on the amateur bands where the maximum output powers used are far lower. Problems with strong signals can be experienced on the amateur bands though, especially on the 40 metre band due to its very close proximity to the 41 metre broadcast band.

When considering problems of overloading in the early stages of a radio receiver it is necessary to bear in mind that most of a receiver's selectivity is provided at the IF stages, and not at the RF and mixer stages at the input of the receiver. Therefore, although a receiver may be tuned to just one fairly weak signal, the wide bandwidth of the RF and mixer stages means that these could be handling a large number of strong signals on nearby channels. This would be of no importance if it was not for the fact that these strong signals can produce signals at frequencies within the IF passband, and which will therefore interfere with the wanted signal. If the RF and mixer stages have perfect linearity, then the intermodulation distortion that produces the unwanted signals will not be produced and there will be no problem. Unfortunately, no active electronic circuits have perfect linearity, and many of the mixer circuits employed in superhet receivers rely on the non-linearity of the mixer transistor in their method of operation! Therefore all superhet receivers suffer from this effect to a lesser or greater degree.

This effect is known as "cross modulation", and when listening on the short wave broadcast bands this can sometimes live up to its name with the modulation of one station being heard in addition to the modulation of the station to which the set is tuned. If the receiver has an RF gain control or aerial attenuator control, backing this control off somewhat will often result in the elimination of the secondary modulation. When listening on the short wave amateur bands, where SSB CW predominate, it is unlikely that cross modulation will manifest itself in this manner, and even when listening on the broadcast bands it may appear in a less obvious way. It is likely to be heard simply as a rather high background noise level which will decrease if the RF gain or aerial attenuator control is backed off slightly. What is important to note here, is that the noise should fall by a far greater amount than proper signals within the passband of the receiver, and by turning back the RF gain or attenuator control it may well be found that wanted signals which were formerly lost under the noise level emerge above the noise!

All that is happening here is that the strong signals that cause the intermodulation do so by overloading the RF and mixer stages of the receiver so that serious distortion results in

these stages, with subsequent severe cross modulation. By
backing off the RF gain or aerial attenuator controls the
interfering signals are reduced to a level where they no longer
cause severe distortion, and the cross modulation signal reduces
by a very large amount, even though there may have been only
a quite small reduction in the sensitivity of the set. Thus, when
cross modulation is proving troublesome it is usually advisable
to have an input signal level which is no higher than absolutely
necessary, and have the IF and AF gain levels quite high in
order to compensate for the small input signal level.

Not all short wave receivers have an aerial attenuator or RF
gain control, but it is very easy to add a variable attenuator
between the aerial and the receiver. Figure 29 shows the circuit
diagram of a simple variable aerial attenuator, and this is just a
1k linear (carbon track, not wirewound) potentiometer used
volume control style. The only other components needed are
the input and output sockets, a small metal box, a control knob,
and the coaxial output lead. Note that the output of the unit
must couple to both the aerial and earth sockets of the receiver i
the unit is to function properly. Using a single lead from the
slider of VR1 to the aerial socket of the receiver and no

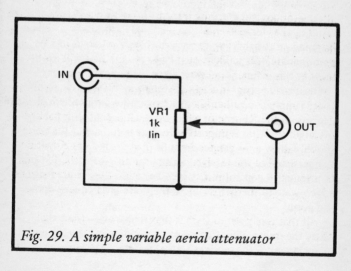

Fig. 29. A simple variable aerial attenuator

connection from the lower track connection of VR1 to the earth socket will result in the unit being very ineffective, with a maximum attenuation level of perhaps only a few dB.

In some cases it might be found that the use of an external aerial attenuator is better at combatting cross modulation than the RF gain control of the receiver. This depends on the precise design of the receiver concerned, but if backing off the RF gain control seems to give only a minor improvement in cross modulation performance it might be worthwhile trying an external aerial attenuator instead.

Additional Selectivity

Figure 30 shows the circuit diagram of a simple aerial attenuator that gives added RF selectivity, as well as providing a variable amount of attenuation at the input of the receiver.

The point of having increased RF selectivity is simply that it reduces the strength of signals fed to the receiver, except in the case of the desired transmission. This reduces the risk of cross modulation but does not weaken the desired signal which is obviously preferable to a straight forward aerial attenuator. A simple tuned filter at the input of a receiver will only give a modest improvement in the RF selectivity of the receiving equipment as a whole, but a worthwhile improvement will often result from adding a simple circuit of the type shown here. A unit of this type also reduces the image response and other spurious responses of the receiver, of course.

The circuit really just consists of a tuned circuit fed with the aerial signal via a low value capacitor, and feeding the input of the receiver via a second low value capacitor and the attenuator control. The only complication is that in order to cover the full short wave spectrum it is necessary to have three switched coils in the tuned circuit due to the wide frequency span that must be covered. L3 is switched into circuit on range 1 and gives coverage from about 1.6 to 5MHz, L2 is switched into circuit on range 2 and gives coverage of approximately 5 to 15MHz, and with L1 switched in on range 3 the frequency coverage is about 12 to 32MHz. VC1 is the tuning control and is switched across the appropriate inductor by one pole of the wavechange switch

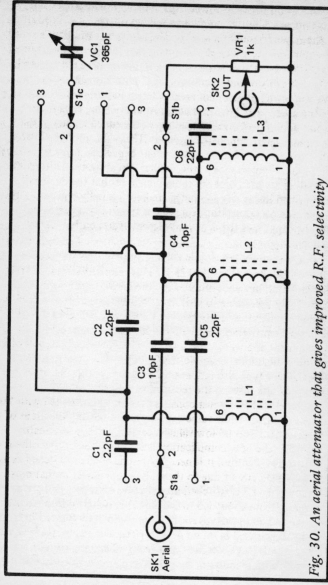

Fig. 30. An aerial attenuator that gives improved R.F. selectivity

(S1c). The three tuning inductors are ready made types and there are actually two coupling windings on each coil in addition to the required tuning winding. The additional windings are just ignored. Note also that the manufacturers range numbers for these coils are 3 to 5, and not the 1 to 3 used here (the range 1 and 2 coils in the manufacturers range numbering are medium and long wave types which are not required in this application).

The purpose of the input and output coupling capacitors is to give a fairly low level of loading on the tuned circuit so that reasonably sharp tuning is obtained. These also produce losses, but these are not as great as one might expect, and this is obviously not of great importance in this application anyway. Different capacitors are used on each tuning range so that the degree of loading and losses on each range are kept virtually constant. The impedance of a capacitor decreases as frequency is increased, and the capacitors therefore have lower values on the higher frequency ranges.

The attenuator is a simple volume control type using a low value carbon potentiometer, as in the previous circuit. The reason for using a carbon potentiometer rather than a wirewound type in applications such as this, incidentally, is that wirewound potentiometers can have a level of inductance that makes them unusable in high frequency applications.

Components for Aerial Attenuator (Figure 30)
   Capacitors

C1	2.2pF ceramic	C2	2.2pF ceramic
C3	10pF ceramic	C4	10pF ceramic
C5	22pF ceramic	C6	22pF ceramic
VC1	365pF air spaced (Jackson type 0)		

   Potentiometer
VR1   1k lin carbon
   Inductors
L1   Denco Transistor usage coil, blue aerial range 5T
L2   Denco Transistor usage coil, blue aerial range 4T
L3   Denco Transistor usage coil, blue aerial range 3T
   Switch
S1   3 way 4 pole rotary type (only three poles used)

Miscellaneous

Case

Two coaxial sockets (SK1 and SK2)

Two control knobs

Three B9A valveholders (coilholders)

Wire, solder, etc.

Construction

The unit is constructed using point-to-point wiring, as shown in
Figure 31. The three coils are fitted in B9A valveholders to
prevent the plastic formers being damaged (which could easily
occur if connections were to be made direct to the pins of the
coils). The six fixed value capacitors are mounted direct on
S1. The two points marked "A" in the diagram are connected
together, as are the two points marked "B" and the two points
marked "C". Try to keep the wiring as short and direct as
reasonably possible.

A coaxial cable must be used at the output of the unit so
that the chassis of the attenuator couples to the chassis or earth
connection of the receiver, as well as coupling the aerial signal
to the receiver. The unit will otherwise fail to function properly.
A coaxial cable at the output of the unit will also ensure that
there is no significant signal pick-up here, so that the attenuator
unit is able to give optimum efficiency. Use a fairly short
connecting cable, preferably no more than about half a metre
long.

In use S1 is used to select the appropriate tuning range, and
VC1 is adjusted to peak the desired signal. This control will
need slight readjustment each time the receiver's tuning control
is adjusted significantly as the tuning of the unit is reasonably
sharp (but not sharp enough to warrant fitting a slow motion
drive to the tuning control). VR1 is backed-off, as necessary,
in order to avoid severe cross modulation.

It is unlikely that the cores of the coils will need any
adjustment in order to give the unit the appropriate frequency
coverage.

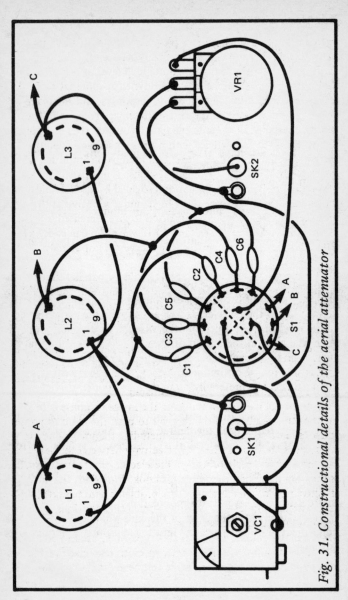

Fig. 31. Constructional details of the aerial attenuator

Tunable Notch Filter

With a few exceptions, short wave receivers are of the super-heterodyne type, and circuits of this type, even if of only a fairly basic specification, give a quite high level of performance. The main drawback of a superheterodyne (or superhet for short) receiver is that it has spurious responses, and the main spurious responses are at the IF and the image response. The spurious response at the intermediate frequency (IF) is simply due to signals at frequencies within the IF passband leaking through the RF and mixer stages and then being amplified and processed in the usual way. This response is not usually much of a problem since the attenuation provided by the RF and mixer stages is likely to be quite high, and a wavetrap at the intermediate frequency is often fitted to give increased attenuation at this response (and an IF wavetrap can easily be fitted in series with the aerial if the receiver is not already equipped with one).

A wavetrap merely consists of an ordinary parallel tuned circuit having a resonant frequency at the centre of the frequency band which is to be attenuated, and it is connected in series with the signal path. A well known property of a parallel tuned circuit is that it has a very high impedance at or near resonance (in fact it theoretically has an infinite impedance at resonance). The wavetrap therefore blocks signals at or close to its resonant frequency, but signals at frequencies significantly off resonance are able to pass without being attenuated.

The normal method of reducing the image response is to use the RF selectivity of the receiver to peak the main response and attenuate all other responses, including the image one. It is also possible to add extra RF selectivity between the aerial and the receiver, perhaps using a preselector or attenuator such as the ones described earlier in this book. However, the most effective way of overcoming severe problems with breakthrough on the image response (or possibly some other spurious response) is usually the use of a rejection filter, like an IF wavetrap. Of course, a filter of this type when used to combat the image response or some similar spurious response must be made tunable, and to cover a wide frequency range, so that it can be used to provide attenuation at the required frequency (which will vary according to the setting of the tuning control of the receiver).

Practical Circuit

The circuit diagram of Figure 32 is for a practical tunable notch filter, and this covers slightly more than the entire short wave spectrum in its three tuning ranges. The circuit is simply a parallel tuned circuit connected in the aerial lead (like an IF wavetrap) with VC1 forming the capacitive section of the tuned circuit, and whichever coil is selected using S1 acting as the inductive section. The frequency coverage is about 1.6 to 5.5MHz with L1 switched in, about 4.8 to 15.5MHz with L2

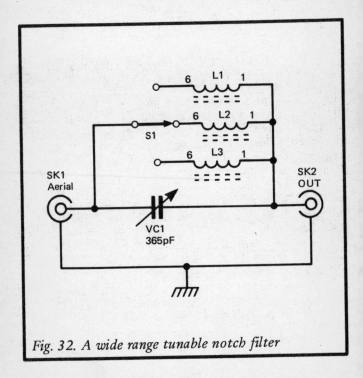

Fig. 32. A wide range tunable notch filter

especially when listening to stations towards the low frequency end of the short wave spectrum (i.e. around 2 to 3MHz). If problems of this type are experienced it would be possible to replace S1 with a four way switch and add an extra range to the unit, with a Range 2T coil being used in the additional switch position. This would enable the filter to be tuned over the medium wave band. However, it is unlikely that this modification will be necessary as the breakthrough of medium wave stations is not usually a serious problem.

Breakthrough of signals in the VHF spectrum can sometimes be a problem, and the filter cannot be used to null interfering signals of this type. If problems with VHF breakthrough are experienced it is probably better to use a low pass aerial filter, rather than try to modify this design to notch out the interfering signals.

One final point concerns the construction of the unit. As will probably be apparent to most readers, the chassis of VC1 should not be allowed to come into contact with the metal case as this would short circuit the aerial signal to earth. A simple way of mounting VC1 so that its chassis is insulated from the case is to glue a small plastic panel to the front plate of VC1, and then glue the plastic panel to the front panel of the case (with both the plastic panel and front panel being drilled with a hole about 14mm in diameter to accommodate the spindle of VC1).

Components for Tunable Notch Filter (Figure 32)
   Capacitors
VC1   365pF air spaced (Jackson type 0)
   Inductors
L1   Denco transistor usage coil, Blue aerial Range 3T
L2   Denco transistor usage coil, Blue aerial Range 4T
L3   Denco transistor usage coil, Blue aerial Range 5T
   Switch
S1   3 way 4 pole rotary switch (only one pole used)
   Miscellaneous
Two coaxial sockets (SK1 and SK2)
Case
Three B9A valveholders

Control knobs
Wire, solder, etc.

Low Pass Aerial Filter

A form of interference which is quite common when listening
on the high frequency short wave bands, but is little understood
by most short wave enthusiasts, is that of VHF signals breaking
through. VHF Band 2 broadcast stations are the usual source
of this type of interference, and can be very troublesome if a
short wave receiver is used in fairly close proximity to a powerful
Band 2 broadcast transmitter. However, interference from radio
telephones and other VHF, or possibly even UHF transmissions
can cause problems.

The cause of this type of interference is simply harmonics on
the output of the local oscillator of the receiver (or first local
oscillator in the case of a multiple conversion receiver). These
harmonics will heterodyne with any incomeing signals at
suitable frequencies to produce an output within the IF passband
of the receiver. The harmonics are at frequencies which are
multiples of the fundamental oscillator frequency, and are
therefore at much higher frequencies than the main oscillator
signal. Accordingly, input signals must be at much higher
frequencies than the normal reception frequency in order to
produce an output from the mixer that is within the IF passband
of the receiver. With the receiver operating on the high
frequency bands this brings the spurious responses into the
VHF spectrum.

Short wave receivers are normally designed to have a
reasonably pure oscillator signal, but most designs still have a
strong enough harmonic content on the oscillator signal to
produce quite strong spurious responses. These responses are
obviously attenuated to quite a high degree by the RF and
mixer tuned circuits of the receiver, but with a sensitive receiver
and very strong signals being picked-up on the spurious responses
this can still lead to problems with breakthrough.

Filter

There are two ways of trying to counteract this type of
through; modifying the receiver to improve the purity
oscillator signal, and adding a low pass filter between the
and the receiver so that the interfering signals are reduced ⌐ an
insignificant level. The first method would be difficult to
implement in practice, and probably few short wave enthusiasts
would be prepared to attempt a modification of this type anyway.
The second method is probably far more practical and requires
the addition of a very simple filter that can be built very
easily and at low cost by the home-constructor. Figure 34
shows the circuit diagram of a filter of this type.

This is just a straight forward single section L–C low pass
filter. L1 has a value which gives a fairly low impedance at
frequencies within the short wave spectrum, but at higher
frequencies its impedance is relatively high. It therefore provides
an easy passage for short wave signals, but tends to attenuate
VHF signals, especially those well into the VHF spectrum. C1
has a value which produces a high impedance at frequencies
within the short wave spectrum, but at higher (VHF) frequencies

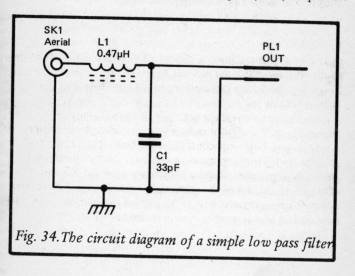

Fig. 34. The circuit diagram of a simple low pass filter

. ipedance becomes much lower. The potential divider action across L1 and C1 therefore gives small losses at frequencies up to the 30MHz upper limit of the short wave spectrum, but quite high losses at frequencies above this limit.

Obviously the unit does give small losses at frequencies within the short wave spectrum, especially at the high frequency end, but these are so small as to give no significant reduction in performance. The attenuation provided at the low frequency end of the VHF spectrum (around 30 to 50MHz) is not very high as the filter has a nominal attenuation rate of 12dB per octave (i.e. a doubling of frequency produces a 75% reduction in sensitivity). However, it is at frequencies of around 100MHz or more that interfering signals are likely to be evident, and the filter gives around 20dB or more of attenuation (i.e. a 90% reduction in sensitivity at least) at these frequencies. This will normally be sufficient to render interfering signals completely insignificant, but if necessary further attenuation can be obtained by using two filters connected in series. This will give increased losses at frequencies with the short wave range as well, but even at the highest frequencies within this range it is unlikely that a serious reduction in performance will occur.

Construction

The filter can be built into a standard Denco screening can or any similar small aluminium container. The screw-on-lid is fitted with a coaxial socket and a soldertag is fitted on one of the 6BA mounting bolts for this in order to provide a convenient chassis connection point. The opposite end of the screening can is drilled to take the coaxial output lead, and it is advisable to fit this hole with a grommet to protect the lead. The output lead should be a fairly loose fit in the grommet so that the lead will not become twisted when the lid of the screening can is screwed in place. The lead must be quite short (no more than about 50 to 100mm long) or it will add a significant capacitance in parallel with C1 and seriously affect the performance of the filter by producing significant losses at pass frequencies. This should not be a problem in practice as the filter is small and it is unlikely that there will be any difficulties in fitting it close to the aerial socket of the receiver. The output lead is, of course, terminated in a connector or connectors that match the aerial/earth socket(s) of the receiver.

The leads of L1 are cut short and it is simply wired between the inner conductor of the output lead and the inner terminal of SK1. Some insulation tape is wound around L1 to ensure that no accidental short circuits to chassis occur, but first C1 is wired between the junction of L1 and the output lead, and the soldertag chassis connection point. C1 should be a ceramic type (plate or disc) and should have its leadout wires trimmed as short as reasonably possible. The outer braiding of the output lead is connected to the soldertag and the filter is then complete.

If it proves necessary to add a second filter, do not build two filters into one case unless the two sections are properly screened off from one another, or it is likely that VHF signals will tend to leak from one filter section to the other with a serious reduction in the effectiveness of the circuit. If the filter gives little reduction in the interference this probably indicates that the interfering signals are not within the VHF spectrum. Alternatively, it could be that they are VHF signals but are being picked-up in the wiring of the receiver, although this is unlikely and would be difficult to combat as this would necessitate modifications to the receiver.

Aerial Tuning Unit

An aerial tuning unit is one of the most useful accessories for a short wave receiver which is used in conjunction with a long wire aerial. The main reason for using an aerial tuning unit (commonly abbreviated to ATU) is that it gives a worthwhile increase in signal strengths; an increase of two or three "S" points being quite normal. This may seem an unlikely claim since an aerial tuning unit is a passive device! However, the claim is a boost in signal strengths, and not that an aerial tuning unit provides gain.

How then, does an aerial tuning unit provide the increase in signal strengths? It does so simply by improving the efficiency of the receiving equipment, and it simply provides a more efficient signal transfer from the aerial to the receiver. An ATU relies on the fact that the source impedance of the aerial signal is likely to be very different to the input impedance of the receiver, and that a quite inefficient signal transfer will therefore result if the aerial is coupled direct to the aerial terminal of the receiver. The aerial tuning unit acts as a sort of matching transformer which ensures that the impedances "seen" by the aerial and receiver are correct, giving a more efficient signal transfer and a consequent boost in signal strengths.

Of course, at some frequencies it is possible that the source impedance of the aerial signal will be a good match for the input impedance of the receiver, and that the addition of an aerial tuning unit will have little or no effect. However, in practice an aerial tuning unit almost invariably provides a worthwhile improvement in performance.

Apart from an increase in signal strengths, an aerial tuning unit has the further beneficial effect of reducing spurious responses of the receiver. This is achieved merely because an aerial tuning unit is a tuned transformer which therefore increases the RF selectivity of the receiving equipment.

Practical Circuit

The circuit of Figure 35 shows a practical arrangement for an aerial tuning unit, and this is a slight modification of the standard type tuning unit circuit. Conventionally a unit of this type consists of a single coil, usually about 25mm in diameter, and having around 50 turns with about six to twelve tappings. A switch is used to select the desired tapping point. A problem with this arrangement is that the coil has to be home constructed, and it can be difficult to obtain suitable parts as well as being awkward to construct the coil.

In this circuit the problem has been overcome by the use of three ready-made coils; the desired coil being selected using S2. This gives fewer inductance values than using a multitapped coil, but using two different types of receiver and aerials of various lengths it was always found to be possible to peak signals on any band using this circuit. It will not work well with a short aerial, and it is not recommended for use with an aerial less than about 6 metres long, but conventional aerial tuning units do not

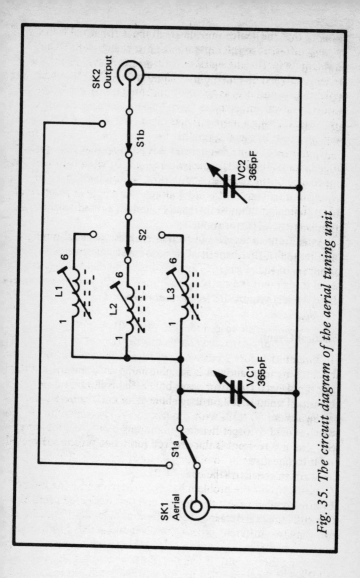

Fig. 35. The circuit diagram of the aerial tuning unit

usually work well with very short antennas either.

The circuit operation of a unit of this type is very straight forward. The selected coil forms a single wound transformer having a capacitive tapping formed by VC1 and VC2, with the tapping connected to earth. By adjusting VC1 and VC2 it is possible to effectively move the tapping point so as to give the desired impedance matching, and these two components must also give a capacitance value that keeps the coil resonant at the reception frequency. Using three switched coils enables the unit to be brought to resonance on any short wave band, as mentioned earlier. L1 is used on the low frequency bands up to about 4 or 5MHz, L2 is used on the low and high frequency bands between about 5 and 15MHz, and L3 is used on the high frequency bands from about 15 to 30MHz.

S1 is simply a bypass switch that enables the aerial tuning unit to be readily removed from the aerial signal path when it is not required.

Components for Aerial Tuning Unit (Figure 35)
  Capacitors
VC1   365pF air spaced (Jackson type O)
VC2   365pF air spaced (Jackson type O)
  Inductors
L1   Denco transistor usage blue aerial coil, range 3T
L2   Denco transistor usage blue aerial coil, range 4T
L3   Denco transistor usage blue aerial coil, range 5T
  Switches
S1   DPDT toggle switch
S2   3 way 4 pole rotary switch (only one pole used)
  Miscellaneous
Two coaxial sockets (SK1 and SK2)
Case
Control knobs
Three B9A valveholders
Wire, solder, etc.

Construction

Figure 36 shows the wiring of the aerial tuning unit. Many of

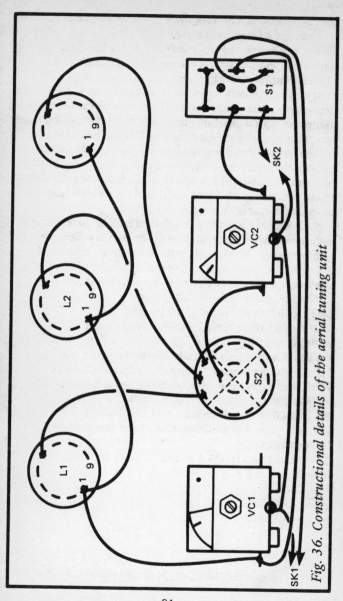

Fig. 36. Constructional details of the aerial tuning unit

the constructional notes for the previous projects also apply to this one and will not be repeated here.

The positions of the adjustable cores of L1 and L2 is not too important, and simply unscrewing these so that about 10mm of metal screwthread protrudes from the top of each of these coils should give satisfactory results. It will probably be necessary to unscrew the core of L3 somewhat further than this in order to get the unit to operate right up to the 30MHz upper limit of the short wave spectrum.

The output of the aerial tuning unit is coupled to the receiver via a reasonably short twin cable. It is not necessary for this to be a coaxial cable, and it is in fact probably better to use an ordinary twin lead which will have a lower capacitance between the two conductors.

Adjusting the unit for best results is really a matter of trial and error with VC1 and VC2 being adjusted in turn to peak the received signal. If adjustments do not seem to make much difference to the strength of the received signal try altering the settings of VC1 and VC2 completely and then repeat the peaking procedure, or switching in a different coil using S2 might help.

It may be rather time consuming to initially find the best settings for VC1, VC2 and S2 for each of the bands on which the equipment is used, but once the optimum settings have been found they can be noted down so that on future occasions when the equipment is used the aerial tuning unit can be quickly peaked. A simple scale calibrated from (say) 0 to 10 can be marked around the control knobs of VC1 and VC2 and will make it easy to note down the optimum settings for these two controls.

For those who prefer a conventional aerial tuning unit, a suitable circuit is provided in Figure 37.

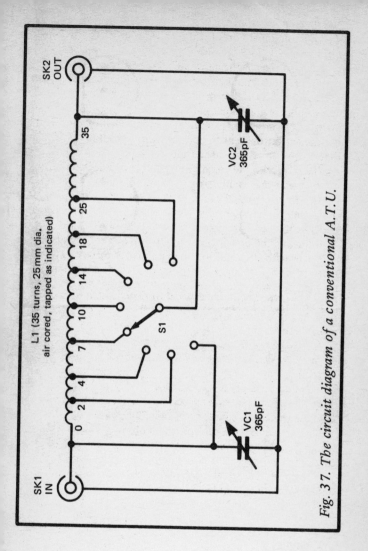

Fig. 37. The circuit diagram of a conventional A.T.U.

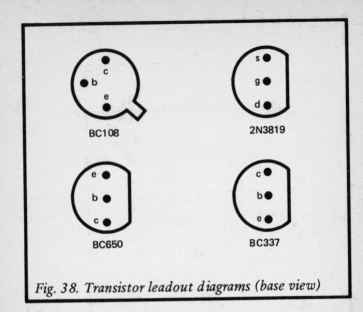

Fig. 38. Transistor leadout diagrams (base view)

Please note overleaf is a list of other titles that are available in our range of Radio, Electronics and Computer Books.

These should be available from all good Booksellers, Radio Component Dealers and Mail Order Companies.

However, should you experience difficulty in obtaining any title in your area, then please write directly to the publisher enclosing payment to cover the cost of the book plus adequate postage.

If you would like a complete catalogue of our entire range of Radio, Electronics and Computer Books then please send a Stamped Addressed Envelope to:

BERNARD BABANI (publishing) LTD
THE GRAMPIANS
SHEPHERDS BUSH ROAD
LONDON W6 7NF
ENGLAND